Dick King-Smith

TRIFFIC PIG BOOK

JOKES

FAB FACTS

QUIZZES AND GAMES

PARTY GUZZLES

SUPER STORIES

DID YOU KNOW?

DAILY PORKER

PIGTURES

GRUNTS 'N' GIGGLES

PIG PERSONALITIES

VICTOR GOLLANCZ LTD
LONDON 1991

Q · What do you call a pig who's a bad actor?

A · A ham

Introduction

There's an old saying — "Beauty is in the eye of the beholder" — which means roughly that we each have our own ideas about what's beautiful and what's not.

For me, the pig is beautiful.

O.K. so it's not graceful like the gazelle, or speedy like the cheetah, or majestic like the lion, or agile like the monkey, but to my eye none of that matters.

I can't understand why everybody else doesn't feel the same way. I mean, you've only got to look at a pig to see that every bit of it is infinitely lovely. No other animal can compete.

Start with that wonderful strong snout with its pair of ducky little nostrils. What a nose!

And then those ears — some sticking up, masterfully, some flopping down, elegantly: great, aren't they? ("Hear, hear!" you should be saying.)

And that body! Compact, sturdy, massive, solid, stout, weighty, imposing — there's no end of words to describe it, as it moves on those four delicious little sharp trotters, daintily, like a dancer.

And behind the behind (and what a masterpiece that is) behold that unique tail, curled like a corkscrew, tipped with the dearest little tuft, the perfect ending.

Have you noticed — I didn't mention the pig's eyes.

I left them till last on purpose, because it is into them that you must look, long and hard.

Other animals cannot stand to be stared at by a human being. Even the tiger, it is said, will turn its head aside.

But not the pig. You'll find that you will be the first to look away.

But before you do, you cannot fail to see in the depths of those piggy eyes a gleam of the highest intelligence.

For the pig, I tell you solemnly — without a word of a lie, honest Injun, no kidding, Scout's honour, see this wet see this dry, cross my heart and hope to die — is the brightest of beasts.

Beauty and Brains — what a combination.

Can you blame me for having a mania about pigs? They are Triffic!

Q. What's a pig's best karate move?

A. A Pork chop

Pig of The Pops

KYLIE MINOGUE – I Should Be So Mucky

PORK McCARTNEY – If Pigs Had Wings

WHITNEY HOUSTON – I'm Your Piglet Tonight

MC HAMMER – Pork It Up

PIG SHOP BOARS – Being Boaring

WET WET WET – I Feel Swine

PIG FLOYD – Pigs On The Wing

JASON DONOVAN – Swilly Sties

ELTON JOHN – Pigball Wizard

TINA TROTTER – Big Fat Dancer

PIGGY SLOP – Wild One

MUDDY HOLLY – Piggy Sue (reissue)

MANEURYTHMICS – The Miracle Of Mud

NEW PIGS ON THE BLOCK – Hammin' Trough

PRINCE – Swine o' The Times

CHER – The Slurp Slurp Song (remix)

MICHAEL JACKSON – Swiller

MADONNA – Piggy Don't Preach

THE MEATLES – Twist And Snout

DAVE BOWIE – Piggy Sawdust

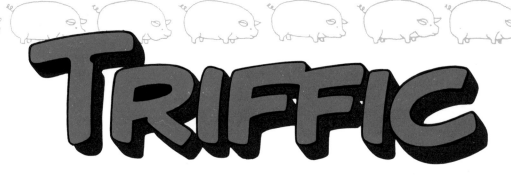

TRIFFIC

Chapter 1

Only One Girl

"Only one girl?" cried Mrs Berkshire in tones of horror.

"'Fraid so," came the unhappy voice of Mrs Tamworth. "The other five are all boys."

"Oh, I am sorry!" said Mrs Berkshire.

For a moment longer she stood, her front trotters resting on top of the wall that separated their two sties, staring into the dark interior where mother and children lay. Then she heaved her bulk back down and addressed her neighbour on the other side, Mrs Gloucester Old-Spots.

"Glossy!" she called.

"What is it, Betty?"

"Teresa Tamworth has farrowed."

"All well, I trust? How many piglets has she?"

"Six. But there's only one girl."

"Oh dear, oh dear!" grunted Mrs Old-Spots, and she made haste, Betty Berkshire could hear, to pass this disturbing piece of news on down the line of pigsties. So that in a matter of moments Molly Middle-White, Sarah Saddleback and Laetitia Large-Black all knew that poor Teresa Tamworth's litter contained — sad to say — only one girl.

"What a shame!" they said, and, "The pity of it!" and there was much tut-tutting and shaking of heavy heads as the five other sows at the Rare Breeds Survival Centre discussed (in low voices) the Tamworth tragedy. A common or garden pig on an ordinary farm might care not at all about the sexes of her newborn children, but for a sow of a Rare Breed it was a very different matter.

Mrs Tamworth's male piglets, the little hogs, were in general merely destined for the butcher, but their sister the gilt, the little female, was precious beyond belief. In due course she would become a mother herself and thus increase the numbers of her kind, making her particular Rare Breed that much less rare.

This was true of all the animals in the Survival Centre, the cows hoping desperately for heifer calves, the sheep for ewe lambs, the mares for filly foals, and the hens for pullets. Only thus could the spectre of extinction, a fate that had already overtaken so many of the old breeds of British livestock, be kept at bay.

And Teresa Tamworth had had only one girl!

"Her first farrow, I believe," said Laetitia Large-Black to Sarah Saddleback, experienced mothers both. "Let us hope she does not overlay any of them."

"Especially the girl," said Sarah. "That would be too dreadful."

Molly Middle-White grunted in sympathy, but she could not keep a look of smug satisfaction off her squashed-in face, for she was nursing a litter of eight, of which six were female.

Meanwhile, back in her sty Teresa lay, deep in straw and thought, suckling her six baby Tamworths. Sandy-red in colour like their mother, they nuzzled greedily at her, none more greedily than the solitary girl who was already shoving her brothers out of the way at the milk bar. Their hunger at last satisfied, they slept, and Teresa got carefully to her feet.

Betty Berkshire's head appeared over the wall.

"Everything all right, dear?" she said.

 Q · What does a pig wear when it's raining?
A · A sow'wester

"Yes," said Teresa.

She sighed deeply.

"If only they could all have been girls," she said.

"Now, now," said Betty briskly. "You mustn't fret. It could happen to any sow."

She needs something to take her mind off it, she said to herself. I know — choosing names. That'll divert her.

"What are you going to call them?" she said.

"I hadn't thought," said Teresa.

"Not that it matters much what you choose for the boys — Tom, Dick or Harry, any old name will do," said Betty. "In fact I shouldn't bother if I was you. But the girl, now that's different. Specially as she's the only one. Be nice to call her something quite out of the ordinary, something no pig has ever been called before."

"Like what?"

"Oh, I don't know — something posh, Guinevere, Hyacinth, Ermintrude, that sort of name."

"I'll think about it," said Teresa.

She thought about it over the next week, while the six little Tamworths grew bigger and stronger, and began to run about the sty and play games. These mostly took the form of mock fights, and the girl, Teresa noticed, easily held her own against any of her brothers.

She's a proper little tomboy, thought Teresa with a mixture of pride and a tinge of regret that her only daughter was not more ladylike. I can't possibly call her by any of the sort of names Betty suggested. Maybe I'd better let her choose her own name. I'll ask her.

"Children!" she called, and when they all came rushing up she said, "Now you boys go and play quietly in the straw for a little while. I have something to say to your sister."

"Tell her not to be so rough, Mum," said one of the little hogs. "She's always beating us up."

"Girls didn't ought to be like that," said another.

"Girls *ought not* to be like that," said Teresa automatically.

"That's right!" they all shouted. "You tell her, Mum!" and they ran off grumbling.

"Wimps!" said the little gilt scornfully.

"Listen, dear," said Teresa. "I think it's time you had a proper name. It doesn't matter so much with the others, I can just say 'Boys!' if I want to call them, but since you're the only girl, I think it would be nice if you had a name of your own."

"Triffic!" said the little gilt.

"Would you like that?"

"Triffic!"

"Perhaps you'd like to choose your own name?" said Teresa.

"But Mum, I don't know any names."

"Well, shall I choose for you?"

"Yes! Triffic!" said the little gilt again.

How fond of that word she seems to be, thought Teresa, and then suddenly Betty Berkshire's words came into her mind. 'Call her something quite out of the ordinary, something no pig has ever been called before.'

Triffic Tamworth! It had quite a ring to it.

Vanity Pig

"You've given me an idea," she said, and she shoved her long ginger snout against the piglet's ear and whispered.

"Weeeee!" squealed the little gilt, and she ran at the biggest of her brothers and knocked him flying.

"What are you playing at?" he gasped, and, "Who do you think you are?" cried the other four hogs, and loudly and proudly their only sister answered, "I'm Triffic, I am!"

Late that afternoon, when the pigman came to give the sows their evening meal, he threw open the door of Teresa Tamworth's sty — for she was first in line — and, while the piglets played around his feet, he said, as always, "All right, old lady?"

The pigman called all the sows 'old lady', whether they were young like Teresa, middle-aged like Betty Berkshire, Sarah Saddleback, Glossy Old-Spots and Laetitia Large-Black, or actually elderly like Molly Middle-White.

"I have no idea what you are saying, my good man," grunted Teresa. "And it's a pity you're too stupid to understand me. I could have told you about my daughter's new name."

The pigman poured the food into the trough, and then, as always, he checked on the piglets, counting them on the thick fingers of his large horny hand.

"Only five?" he said. "And them all hogs too? Oh no, old lady — don't tell me you've been and gone and overlaid that little gilt of yours!"

continued on page 12

GROOMING FOR PIGS
Tip No. 1
Teresa Tamworth's Deliciously Grubby Mud pack

You will need:
1 gallon gooey mud (I prefer the thick, clay mud, but you may not be able to dig that up)
1 bucket
1 hour piglet-free
1 quiet corner
1 portion Triffic's Trough Special (see page 33)
1 wall
1 obliging neighbour (Betty Berkshire's a real gem for this one)

When you're ready:
Place mud-filled bucket on top of wall.
Position yourself beneath bucket.
Ask obliging neighbour to knock bucket on to you.
Relax, taking occasional gulps of Triffic's Trough Special.
Wonderful!

9

RECORD PORKERS

'Bud', a crossbred barrow pig from Texas, was the most expensive pig ever. In March 1983 he was bought for $56,000.

Ten babies at one birth may be a record for human mothers, but in 1961 a sow in Denmark gave birth to thirty-four piglets in one litter. Thirty-four piglets were also born in one litter to a Wessex sow on a Kent farm in 1955 (though thirty of these were stillborn). And in 1971 thirty-two piglets were born in Gloucestershire (eight were stillborn). But in 1979 a remarkable thirty piglets were born live to a White Wessex sow in Hertfordshire — that's the highest recorded number in Britain.

The heaviest piglet recorded was a boar from a litter of nine, born in Wiltshire. At weaning (about eight weeks old) this chap weighed 36.7 kg (81 lb) — what a whopper!

The Mini Maialino is the smallest breed of pig and was developed in Italy after years of interbreeding Vietnamese pot-bellied pigs. At birth this tiny pig weighs 400 g (less than a small bag of flour!). When fully grown it still only weighs 9 kg (20 lb).

The heaviest British pig was the Rudgewick, a breed that is now extinct. In 1798 a massive boar weighed in at 739.3 kg (1630 lb).

But if you think that's big. . .
The heaviest pig in the world was a Poland-China hog named 'Big Bill'. Big Bill was due to be exhibited at the 1933 Chicago World Fair when he broke a leg and had to be put down. It's probably just as well as Big Bill tipped the scales at an incredible 1157.5 kg (2552 lb) and was so fat his belly dragged along the ground. Big Bill was stuffed and exhibited for some time in Tennessee. He then passed to a travelling carnival and later mysteriously disappeared. . .
Some pig.

SWINEDOM'S SWIFTEST

You've all heard of horse-racing, greyhound-racing and even pigeon-racing, but who ever heard of a racing pig!

Pigs have been raced in America for quite a while. They seem to love it—partly because they're natural show-offs and enjoy the attention of the crowd, partly because they know there's a biscuit waiting for the lucky winner at the finishing post (and some crumbs for the losers!).

Robinson's Racing Pigs (above) are the best known racing pigs in the States. Since they were launched to stardom in 1985 they've toured the US, Canada and the Caribbean in ten teams of super swift swine. They can sprint 150 metres before you can say Pig Robinson and they've even risked their porky hams on a steeplechase over low jumps!

Daggie Dogfoot, the amazing swimming pig, says:

Their owners and trainers treat them with tender love and care but they're careful not to over do it with titbits, keeping them trim and healthy on a well-balanced diet.

The Americans take their pig-racing very seriously. A swinemaster introduces the individual pigs in their distinctive silks and cheerleaders root for their chosen pig—earning a winner's ribbon if their particular porker is first with his snout past the finishing post.

All this attention sometimes goes to their heads. Take the time two of these squealin' demons were invited to appear on the famous Johnny Carson TV show. After being watched by 12 million viewers these pigs got five star treatment—sleeping overnight in the bathroom of a luxury hotel and being taken on a chauffeur driven tour of Hollywood in a limousine . . . what a pair of pampered porkers!

Q · Why don't pigs hitchhike?

A · They haven't got thumbs

Chapter 2

Octavius

Teresa watched, puzzled, as the pigman hastened into the inner part of the sty and searched anxiously through the straw. Counting was not her strong point, and she noticed nothing amiss until one of the hogs said, "She's gone."

"Who's gone?" asked Teresa.

"Wotsername," said another.

"Gone? Where?" said Teresa.

"Out through the door," said the third.

"The man left it open," said the fourth hog.

"Good riddance," said the fifth.

"Can't understand it," said the pigman, coming out again, and then he saw that he had indeed left the sty door slightly ajar.

"Little madam!" he said. "She's done a bunk!" and he hurried out, bolting the door behind him.

Betty Berkshire's head appeared above the wall.

"What's all the fuss about, dear?" she asked.

"Oh Betty!" said Teresa. "She's gone!"

"Who has?"

"My daughter! My only daughter! She's run away from home. That stupid pigman left the door open and she must have slipped out. Oh dear, oh dear, what am I to do? She's only little, and goodness knows what dangers she may run into out there!"

"Calm yourself, Teresa," said Betty Berkshire. "So long as she is not trodden on by a bull, or kicked by a cart-horse, or squashed by a tractor, she will be quite all right. I will pass the word

along the sties to keep an eye out for her. Have you named her yet?"

"Yes."

"What?"

"Triffic."

"Ah. Hum. Certainly original," said Betty. "Now you just try to relax, dear. A trouble shared is a trouble halved," and off she went to tell the tidings to Glossy and Sarah and Laetitia and Molly.

In a remarkably short space of time almost every animal in the Rare Breeds Survival Centre had heard, on the grapevine, the news of the escape. This rapid spread, of fact or of rumour, was, as always, thanks to the pigeons. In the middle of the Centre's great cobbled yard, flanked by the pigsties, the stables, the cattle-courts and the sheep-pens, stood an ancient dovecot shaped like a giant pepper-pot, in which lived a flock of white fantail pigeons. These birds flew freely about the place, scavenging their food from others' leavings and listening with interest to their gossip. One that was preening itself upon a pigsty wall overheard a conversation between Mrs Large-Black and old Mrs Middle-White, and flew back to the dovecot to spread the word.

Within half an hour it was generally known that a very small Tamworth piglet by the name of Triffic was on the loose, and all eyes were on the lookout for her.

Triffic however was nowhere to be seen.

When first she had nipped out of the sty, she had run and run as fast as her short legs would carry her, from sheer excitement at being free, with no four walls to enclose her and no five wimpish brothers to annoy her. She had run right across the wide cobbled yard, empty of people, for the day's parties of visitors to the Survival Centre had by now all gone home. On the far side she saw an open stable door and dashed inside. Hardly had she flopped down on the floor to catch her breath when she heard a voice.

"Go away, rat," the voice said in deep and mournful tones, "or I'll kick your head off."

Triffic looked up to see a tall grey animal standing at the back of the stable with his rump towards her. He was tethered to a ring fixed in the wooden manger, and now turned his head to look round.

A bony Roman-nosed head it was, with long

splayed ears above it, and the look on the creature's face was melancholy in the extreme. Triffic had no idea what kind of animal it was, but of one thing she was quite certain.

"Excuse me," she said, "but I am *not* a rat. I am a pig. And what's more, I am a Rare Breed of pig."

"Oh, spare us all that guff, do," said the tall grey animal. "That's all they keep on about in this place nowadays, pigs, cattle, sheep, goats, poultry, they're all the same — Rare Breed this and Rare Breed that, makes me sick," and he stamped a hind foot loudly on the floor and pulled a wisp of hay from the rack above his head.

Grumpy old thing, thought Triffic. He can't be Rare from the sound of things but then I don't even know what sort of animal he is. Is he a horse perhaps?

"Are you a horse?" she said.

"My poor mother was," said the grey beast dolefully.

"But you're not?"

"No."

"But if your mother was a horse and your father was a horse, you must be a horse too?"

"My father was a donkey."

"I don't get it," said Triffic.

"I am a mule."

"Oh," said Triffic, puzzled. "I am a Tamworth," she said. "My name's Triffic. What's yours?"

The mule swallowed his mouthful of hay and turned around as far as his halter would allow to look down at the piglet.

"Octavius," he said.

"Sorry?"

The mule sighed deeply.

"Octavius, young miss," he said, "is my name. And before you ask any more questions I will tell you that I am the oldest inhabitant of this so-called Rare Breeds Survival Centre. Which when I was a youngster was an ordinary farm. Except that the farmer of those days did not care for noisy smelly great tractors but preferred to work his land with horses. And not only with horses, but with a team of eight mules. Of which I was the youngest. Hence Octavius."

Triffic looked bewildered.

The mule sighed again.

"I am the sole survivor of that team," he said. "I am very old. I spend a lot of my time alone in this dark stable, alone with my memories of my seven dead mates and of the days of long ago. I have no visitors but the stockman and no company but the rats."

He gave a feeble husky bray, halfway between a groan and a cough, and his long floppy ears flopped even further.

"I have no friends," he said.

How miserable he looks, thought Triffic, and quickly she said, "I'll be your friend, Octavius. If you would like."

At that moment a pigeon alighted in the doorway of the stable and waddled up to the piglet, its white tail fanned out behind it.

"You called Triffic?" it said.

"Yes."

"Talk about needles in haystacks," said the pigeon. "We've been looking everywhere for you. Your mother's in a proper state about you. You'd better get off home," and it flew away back towards the pigsties to break the news.

Triffic waited a moment for Octavius to respond to her offer of friendship, but the old mule merely pulled down another mouthful of hay and munched moodily, his grey back towards her and his tufted bell-pull of a tail hanging limp and listless.

"Goodbye then, Octavius," she said, but he made no answer, so she scampered off back across the yard again.

As she neared the line of pigsties she could see first that there were a number of pigeons strutting along the walls, gobbling and cooing, and second, that as a result all her mother's neighbours were standing resting their trotters on their gates and looking out. And all of them, as she passed, expressed their opinions of this runaway child. No piglet of theirs, they all felt sure, would dream of behaving in such a manner.

"Disgraceful!" grunted Laetitia Large-Black as Triffic passed her sty, and, "Scandalous!" sniffed Sarah Saddleback.

"Worrying your poor mother like that!" grumbled Molly Middle-White, and, "You should be ashamed of yourself!" growled Glossy Old-Spots.

Betty Berkshire merely snorted, but it was a very eloquent snort.

Only Teresa Tamworth was not upon her gate, because that position was already occupied, by the pigman, looking in.

"Try not to worry, old lady," he was saying as Triffic trotted up behind him. "I've searched everywhere for your little girl but I can't find where she's got to."

And inside, though she understood not a word of this, Teresa was saying, "My little girl's on her way home, you stupid fellow, I've just heard. Get off that gate and look about you."

Which, though her grunts meant nothing to him, the pigman did.

Then he saw Triffic.

Then he gave a great gasp of relief.

Then he opened the door and let her in.

"Well I never, old lady!" he cried. "What have you got to say about that?"

Teresa Tamworth had a great deal to say.

Like any mother who has been worried stiff about her child, she felt a mixture of thankfulness and anger, and no one listening, as the other sows all were, could have guessed at her delight that her daughter was safe and sound.

"Naughty, bad, wicked, thoughtless girl!" she stormed. "Only a week old and you go gallivanting about just as you please instead of staying here with me. Why can't you be good and well-behaved like your brothers?"

Triffic did not answer, but the five little hogs looked smug, and the listening sows nodded their heavy heads in approval.

"You are never to run away again," said Teresa. "Do you understand?"

"Yes, Mum," said Triffic.

But don't expect me to stay cooped up in this boring old sty with my snotty little brothers, she thought. For one thing, I'm jolly well going to see poor old Octavius again. And I've got a lot more exploring to do yet.

"I won't run away again, Mum," she said.

I'll walk away instead, she thought.

continued on page 24

PEDIGREES

☞ Q. What do you call a pig that can write with all four trotters?
A. Hambidextrous

All Western breeds of domestic pigs are descended from the Wild Boar (*Sus scrofa*), which was still found in England up until about three hundred years ago. By the end of the eighteenth century, European domesticated pigs had become grossly fat and had to be crossed with small, light-boned pigs brought in from China and South-East Asia, to make, eventually, the farm animals we have today. The modern domestic pig is therefore very much a crossbreed, but it is interesting that it still shows some of the wild pig's behaviour.

Just look at the way modern sows raise their piglets (if allowed the space). The wild pig is an expert bed-maker or nest-builder. Sows about to give birth will gather enormous amounts of vegetation and build a huge circular nest, turning round and round in it to make it comfortable. The modern pig will do the same if it has the freedom and materials. When the litter is born each piglet selects a nipple and sticks to it, defending it against the others. This sometimes creates difficulties in today's pigs when the farmer has to foster piglets from one sow to another.

As well as nest-building, wild pigs like to wallow and to rootle in woodland, looking for food. They do not move about in herds, but rather in family groups of sows and young, the boar usually remaining solitary. Given half a chance,

modern pigs will still behave in the same way. A Roman writer called Columella described what would have been ideal pig-country in his day: 'The most convenient feeding-grounds are woods covered with oaks, cork-oaks, beeches, Turkey oaks, holm-oaks, wild olive trees, terebinth-trees, hazels, junipers, nettle trees, vine-tendrils, cornel-trees, strawberry-trees, plum trees, Christ's thorn and wild pear trees'. What a pig's paradise that would be!

Wild pigs were first raised for food as long ago as 7000 BC. But pig-meat was not popular everywhere. It has always been well-liked in Western Europe but in Eastern Europe, people preferred goat-meat. In China the pig is one of the oldest domesticated animals and the fat-bellied pigs that are still farmed today are of ancient origin. Pig-meat is also eaten by the Pacific Islanders. But it is completely forbidden to all Jews and Muslims, and in Ancient Egypt people thought pigs were dirty. The Greek historian Herodotus wrote: 'If a man in passing accidentally touches a pig, he instantly hurries to the river and plunges in with all his clothes on'. Hard luck on non-swimmers!

A pig party can be great fun, if you remember the following points . . .

1   Remove all small tables, chairs and breakable objects, and push the heavy furniture against the wall.

2   Pigs eat anything and everything, so shut away all cats, dogs, babies, and children too small to get out of the way in time.

3   Allow access to an outside room (the garden) where your guests will make valuable contributions to the future health of your rose-trees.

4   Provide unlimited food of every description. It is not possible to give pigs too much to eat, and they are never sick. Stock up beforehand with (for example) muffins, milkshakes, marshmallows, mangel-wurzels, mushrooms, macaroni cheese, meringues, marmalade, mashed potatoes, maids-of-honour and mulligatawny soup. Mix all this together in one huge bowl and serve.

P.S. (Profitable Stratagem) at the end of the meal there will be no trace of food on the floor, but a final generous sprinkling of muesli will ensure that your carpet receives a thorough hoovering from the guests before they leave.

P.P.S. (Pig Party Suggestion) Don't give one.

But, if you are determined to hold a pig party, you'll find some suggestions in this book for things to make and do. Why not start by making Pig Party invitation cards (page 21), and then there is a pig mask to make on page 20. Get going—and have a fab party!

Q . What do you call a pig with spikes?

A . A porkupine

PIG PARTY

PIN THE TAIL...

You will all know the game of 'Pin the Tail on the Donkey', but have you heard of 'Pin the Tail on the Pig'?

The rules are the same—just trace the outline of a pig from this page, or draw your own. Then make everyone a different coloured tail, using ribbon or strips of paper, and attach Blu- Tack or Plasticine to one end of the tail for easy sticking. Blindfold each player in turn and tell them to stick their tail on the pig. Closest to home wins a prize!

Q · And what would you call it if it was hiding in a bush?

A · A hedgehog

DAILY PORKER

ARTICLES FOR SALE

IMMEDIATE DELIVERY

Trough. Holds 5 gallons swill. Make a hog of yourself and contact *Mr Boarny* on *Berkshire 242*.

Four skis. Only one owner. Free to good home. Ring Tammy at Littlehamton 63.

Due to weather conditions massive discounts

Cecil Swill's mud. Wallow in it! Ring me now — *Bristle 775*.

LADIES

Tail perm kits with free curler. Guaranteed to restore that special curl. From **Sally Saddleback**. *Wessex 654*.

SPECIALISTS IN KENNELS AND RUNS

New Pig Sties. Built to fit. All mod cons. **Warthog's Designs**. *Trott's Castle*, Swinedon 332.

Small, wrought-iron pen gate. Keep those piglets safe! *Ring Horace Hog, Wartown 695*.

GET ANOTHER ONE FREE

Warthog's tuskpaste. In our popular flavours: earth, swill, and our original grub special.

Wind in the pig-pen? Seal it with Hog's Fixit.

for the mature purchaser

Porky's oinkment. Soft as the skin on a piglet's bottom!

Ear-muffs, made from genuine silk purses. *Contact Lilly Lop on Hamchester 887*.

rubbish and unsaleable items

Wallow to your heart's content. Mud by the bucketful. From Hogston Farm. *Snortville 313*.

Look a hog with Mr Pig's instant glue-on bristles. In your local Sty Shop now.

UNDER A TENNER

One tail curler. From Bristling Brenda, Boarton Woods 263.

SERVICES OFFERED

No mess, everything cleared

Mistress Piggy's speedy cleaning service. *Clean sties our speciality.* Ham 221.

Piglet-sitter. Contact Laetitia Large-Black. RBSC 914.

● CLEARANCES ●

Grunt's clearances. Good prices paid for troughs, mud, old straw, etc. **Ring Grunt on Undertrott 444.**

Expert tuition and diet advice

Feeling a little porky? Join Pork-Watchers.

Pigadilly's Restaurant. Enter Hog's heaven. **Pig-swill by the pint! Truffles by the trotterful! Call Pigadilly 32 for bookings.**

"FORGET THE COWBOYS"

DATESWINE. We have simply heaps of burly boars and sultry sows on our books! Your first introduction is free! *Join immediately.* **YOU TOO CAN FIND LOVE.**

Underweight? Don't despair. You too can have a real ground-brushing Vietnamese pot-belly. Contact **Mi Phat Tumm**. *Hanoi 345 (Extension 2)*.

HOLIDAYS

Beat the Squirrels! Wallowe'en Special. Book now for our infamous annual Hunt the Acorns weekend. Special rates for piglets. *Phone Bob or Bessy Berkshire on Eppig 698. Acorn House Hotel, Eppig Forest.*

Truffle hunting in Trotterdam. Spoil yourself and ring *Ronald Rootle*. Rusham Woods 443.

FREE DOOR TO DOOR TRANSPORT

Learn the ancient art of mud wrestling: sow to sow and boar to boar. Weekend courses available now from Will Boar, Porkchester 525.

Stay at Wart Farm for a week of pig luxury.
Shallow heated mud pool
Oil rinses
Rooting pen — replenished hourly!
Details from Wanda Warthog, Wartle 889.

INCREDIBLY LOW SALE PRICES

The Princess and the Pig

A beautiful princess was one day walking along a country road when she saw a large pig sitting on the grass verge.

Being of a kindly nature, she stopped to speak to it.

"Hullo, piggy," she said with a smile.

"Hi," said the pig. "Though actually I'm a handsome youth. I upset the local witch, with the results you can see."

"What did you say to her?" asked the princess.

"I called her a dirty smelly ugly evil old bag," said the pig. "So she put a spell on me. 'Only a kiss from a beautiful princess can change things now', she said, and off she went, cackling with laughter."

"Oh," said the princess.

She looked at the pig doubtfully.

But then, because she was of a kindly nature, she bent down and, shutting her eyes and screwing up her courage, planted a kiss on the end of the pig's rubbery snout.

Immediately the princess also turned into a pig.

Here's just the thing to wear at a pig party after you've guzzled!

Trace the pig's face on to card and cut out. Carefully cut two holes for the eyes, making sure you will be able to see through them.

Decorate the mask, then punch two small holes on each side of the mask, positioned as shown. Thread a piece of string or elastic through these holes — it must be long enough to fit around the back of the head.

If you are holding a pig party, turn a trotter to making your own pig party invitation cards.

For each card you will need:

A piece of stiff paper, measuring 300 mm x 110 mm
Scissors

1 Carefully fold the paper into equal sections concertina fashion, as shown.

2 Trace the half pig above on to the top section of the paper, making sure that the straight edge of the pig is exactly on the fold.

3 With the paper still folded, cut around the pig's outline.

4 Unfold. Now decorate the pigs. Write the date, time and place of your pig party – and don't forget to say which little piggy is sending the invitation!

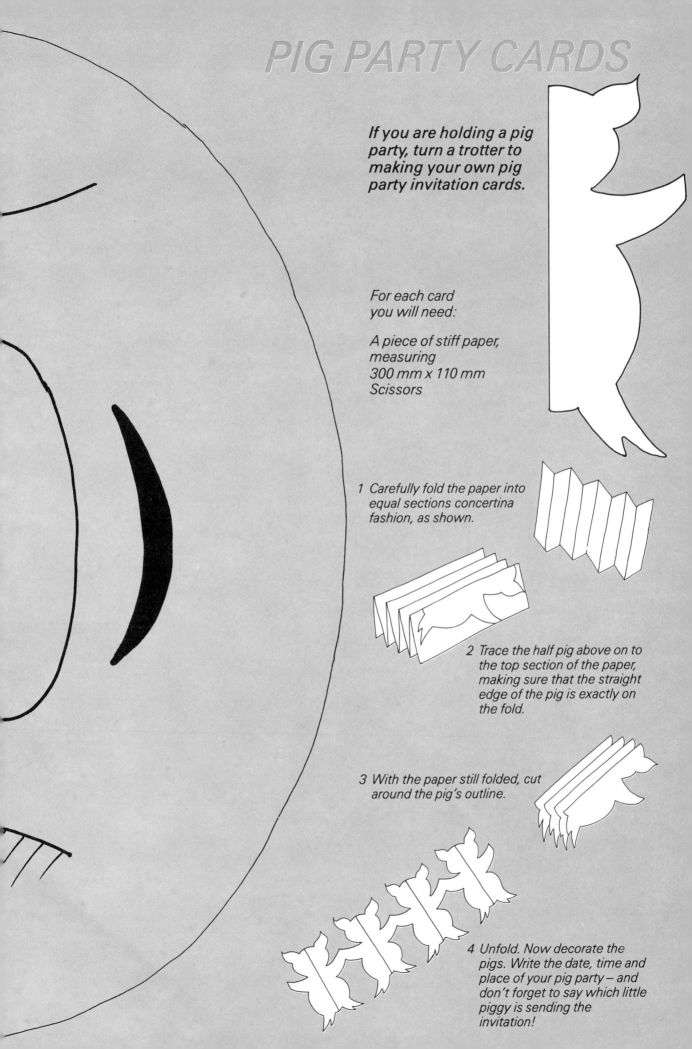

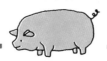

Hogsel and Gruntel

Once upon a time there were two little piglets, brother and sister, called Hogsel and Gruntel. They were very unhappy, for their mother had died and their stepsow was not kind to them, so they ran away, into the forest.

They walked and walked, trotter in trotter, until they were quite exhausted and it seemed that they must die from hunger.

But suddenly they came upon a little house all made of gingerbread, with windows of transparent sugar.

"Saved!" cried Hogsel, and he tore off a piece of the roof and stuffed it in his mouth, while Gruntel helped herself to a window pane.

Just then an ancient crone appeared from inside the little house.

"Come in, little pigs!" she cried. "You are hungry, I can see, so I will heat up the oven." (And stick you both in it, she thought – nothing nicer than roast pork!)

So Hogsel and Gruntel went inside, and the old crone heated up the oven.

"See if it's hot enough," she said. (And then I'll push you both in, she thought.)

"We're not tall enough to see into the oven," said Hogsel, and, "You have a look," said Gruntel, and when the old crone did, they pushed her in and shut the oven door.

While she was cooking, Hogsel and Gruntel polished off all the rest of the little gingerbread house and its sugar windows too. All that was left standing was the oven, from which came a strong smell of cooking crone.

"I'm full," said Gruntel at last.

"Me too," said Hogsel.

"What about her?" said Gruntel.

"I couldn't eat another thing," said Hogsel.

So they left her to stew in her own juice.

P I G S P E A K

Did you know that the pig is featured in many common sayings and expressions? But what do they mean. . .?

PIGS IN CLOVER People who have money but don't know how to behave themselves decently.

PIG IN A POKE A blind bargain.

PIG'S WHISPER A very short space of time (enough for a grunt).

BARTHOLOMEW PIG A very fat person. (At Bartholomew Fair a pig was roasted whole and sold piping hot.)

PIG-HEADED Obstinate.

PIG-IRON Iron cast in oblong ingots. The main channels in which the molten liquid runs are called sows, the smaller branches pigs.

ST ANTHONY'S PIG A pet pig, the patron saint of swineherds. St Anthony is the smallest of the litter.

TO DRIVE ONE'S PIGS TO MARKET To snore loudly.

WHEN PIGS FLY Never.

PIGSKIN A saddle (the best are made of pigskin).

PIG'S TROTTER A mushroom also known as Rubber Brush. Stew in butter, with parsley.

TRIFFIC

Chapter 3

A Comical Pair

In fact another whole week passed before Triffic was able to walk away, for the pigman was now extremely careful about shutting the sty door at feeding times.

Even then it was a matter of luck.

Each morning, before his breakfast, the Manager of the Survival Centre liked to have a wander round and a good look at all the animals in his charge, before the public were admitted.

As it happened, he arrived at the line of sties as the pigman was mucking out Teresa Tamworth, and he leaned on the outer wall, looking in.

"All right, Joe?" he said.

"Yes, Boss," said the pigman. "She's doing 'em well."

"Only one gilt, I think you said?"

"Yes, Boss. Little madam. Look at her now."

The Manager looked, and saw that though the five hogs were frisking around their mother as the pigman swept and shovelled with cries of "Move over, old lady!" the solitary gilt was waiting by the sty door, peering out through the narrow gap between door and hanging post. She looked alert and tense, like a sprinter waiting in the blocks.

"What's she up to?" asked the Manager.

"Wants to do a bunk, doesn't she," said the pigman. "Done one a week ago. I never shut the door proper, truth to tell, and she slipped out. Gone a good hour she was, Lord knows where, I looked all over."

"How did you get her back?"

"She come of her own accord," said the pigman. "Little madam," and he disappeared into the inner part of the sty, shovel in hand.

The Manager walked round to the door and looked over. The piglet looked up at him. The expression in her eyes, he thought, was knowing.

Grinning like a naughty boy, the Manager opened the door a little, expecting the piglet to rush out, and surprised to see that she walked slowly away up the yard. He bolted the door again and followed at a distance, and saw the piglet, still walking in a leisurely manner, disappear into the stable that housed Octavius the mule.

"Hullo, Octavius," said Triffic. "I'm back."

"Yes, I would like that," said Octavius in his gloomy voice.

"Like what?"

"I would like to have you for a friend, young miss," said the old grey mule, continuing their last conversation as if no time had elapsed, though in fact Triffic had doubled her age since then.

"Oh brill!" said Triffic. "I'll come and visit you often."

"Do they let you out of your sty then?" asked Octavius.

"The pigman won't, but just now another man actually opened the door for me."

"What did he look like?"

"Tall and thin, with a lot of hair on the bottom of his face."

Standing by the stable door, out of their sight but listening, the Manager stroked his beard reflectively. He could not of course understand a word, but he could hear the piglet grunting away and the soft snickering noises that the mule made in reply. Peeping round, he saw that they were almost nose to nose, the mule's head bent to the piglet's snout.

I've never seen old Octavius appear so relaxed, almost happy, he thought. Not that he's capable of looking really happy, but he actually seems to have found a friend at last, grumpy old thing.

What a comical pair they make! Anyone would think they were talking to one another!

"That must have been the Boss that let you out," said Octavius. "The stockman, that looks after me, he's a small chap with bow legs."

Even as he said this, a small man appeared at the top of the yard and walked, bow-legged, towards the mule's stable.

"Morning, Boss," he said as he approached. "Just going to take Octavius down to the water tank for a drink."

The Manager held a finger to his lips.

"Quiet a minute, Jim," he said softly. "Have a look in here."

When the stockman saw the odd couple, he took off his greasy old cap and scratched his head.

"Did you ever?" he said.

They watched in silence for a while.

"Never known the old mule allow another animal anywhere near him," said the stockman. "Knock the eye out of a fly, he can, crabby old cuss."

And indeed there was a notice on the stable door:

> **OCTAVIUS**
> Do not approach this mule, sole survivor of an eight-mule team, too closely.
> **He kicks.**

But now when the stockman entered, Octavius did not lay back his long ears or roll his eyes or show his yellow teeth or stamp a warning hoof, but stood, quiet as an old sheep, while the stockman untied his halter and led him out of the stable.

The Manager stood watching as the bony old mule went clip-clopping down over the cobbles, the little piglet scuttling along at his heels. At the same time he saw a large fat figure come hurrying up the yard, looking anxiously about him. When the pigman saw the odd couple, he took off his greasy old cap and scratched his head.

"Did you ever?" he said.

At the water tank, Octavius drank deeply, and then, his thirst quenched, bent his grey head to his friend, while drips of water fell from his velvety muzzle on to her upturned snout.

"Here comes the pigman, young miss," he said. "I expect it's time you went back to your mother, isn't it?"

"O.K. Octavius," said Triffic. "See you again soon."

"I shall look forward to that," said Octavius, and they touched noses, before Triffic turned and trotted on down to the sties, the pigman following.

All the sows were standing up against their doors, the Manager could see, while the fantail pigeons fluttered excitedly about them, and he could hear the loud angry grunting of the Tamworth as she was reunited with her truant child.

"Don't be too hard on her, Teresa," he said out loud. "You may be Rare, but I suspect that piglet of yours is even rarer. The star attraction of the Survival Centre, that's what she's going to be," and off he went to his breakfast, of fried bacon, from a common or garden pig, that had not survived.

25

continued on page 35

THE TAMWORTH

A red pig with prick ears and a long snout. It does well in outdoor conditions and is particularly suitable for very hot countries, such as Australia, where sunburn is a constant problem with white pigs as well as humans! The Tamworth has also bred in sub-zero temperatures, and is probably the hardiest of all breeds.

THE BRITISH LOP

A white pig with, as its name suggests, lop ears. As is usual with lop-eared breeds, this pig has a docile and contented nature and is thus suitable for keeping outdoors. It is thought to be descended from the Cornish White and the Devon Lop, and is closely associated with the Tavistock area in Devon.

THE BRITISH SADDLEBACK

Two types of Saddleback pigs, the Wessex and the Essex, have now been merged to give the British Saddleback. The white saddle varies, some pigs being almost black and others having saddles covering most of their bodies. They are large, lop-eared pigs and the sows have plenty of milk for their babies.

THE GLOUCESTER OLD SPOT

This breed originated in the Severn Valley where it was once called the Orchard Pig because it was traditionally fed on windfall apples and the whey from cheese-making. Lop-eared and hardy, it was once liberally covered with black spots on its white body, but the modern G.O.S. has only a few spots.

BREEDS

THE MIDDLE WHITE

The Middle White has a short head with a turned-up nose that gives its face a very dished or squashed-in look: this in turn makes it disinclined to root, and it is thus less damaging to grassland.

THE LARGE BLACK

The name describes this pig perfectly. It is very docile, and its lop ears and placid temperament means that it needs no elaborate fencing to keep it in – a single strand electric fence is quite enough. As well as hair, the skin has black pigmentation, which protects the animal from sunburn.

THE BERKSHIRE

This pig is relatively small and dark brown or black in general colour, with white feet, a white tail switch, white marking on the snout, and prick ears. Its ancestors were Neapolitan animals which were descended from Chinese pigs.

THE OXFORD SANDY AND BLACK

This breed is sandy in colour (ranging from light sandy to rust) with random black blotches. It has semi-lop to lop ears held close to the face, and is noted for its hardiness, good mothering qualities, and excellent temperament. They can be brainy too. There is a story about an Oxford called The Honourable Annie who was reared with a calf, and who used to pull down a bale of fresh straw each day from the stack for their mutual benefit.

Little Red Riding Pig

Little Red Riding Pig set out one day to visit her grandmother.

She was called Little Red Riding Pig because she was small, of a ginger colour, and always rode about on her BMX bike.

Cycling through a forest glade, she met a wolf.

"Hold it right there, baby," said the wolf.

Little Red Riding Pig held it.

"Where you headin'?" said the wolf.

"To visit my grandmother," replied Little Red Riding Pig.

The wolf thought quickly. Not a lot of meat on this piglet, he said to himself, but the granny – now she might make a square meal.

"Your granny kinda fat?" he asked in a casual way.

"Oh yes!" said Little Red Riding Pig. "She's very fat."

"Sure like to meet her," said the wolf. "She live around here some place?"

"Oh yes!" said Little Red Riding Pig, and she told the wolf how to get to her grandmother's house, and away he went.

When he arrived, he knocked on the door and a voice called, "Come in, my dear," so he did.

There, lying in bed, was the fattest pig the wolf had ever seen.

"Goodness me!" said the pig. "I thought you were my little granddaughter."

"'Fraid not, ma'am," said the wolf.

"But I see now," said Little Red Riding Pig's grandmother, "that you are in fact a handsome stranger. What big ears you have!"

All the better to hear you with, thought the wolf, but he kept his mouth shut.

"And what big eyes you have!"

All the better to see you with, thought the wolf, but he said nothing, merely opening his jaws wide in a kind of silent laugh.

"And what big teeth you have!" said the fat pig, and before the wolf could think about that, she went on, "Which reminds me, I have the toothache. I should be so grateful if you could look and see which tooth is causing the trouble."

"Why, sure, ma'am," said the wolf, and he approached the bed, dribbling slightly at the thought of the feast in store.

The fat pig opened her mouth wide, and the wolf bent his head to look into it.

Not long afterwards Little Red Riding Pig came pedalling up on her BMX. Usually, when she knocked on the door, her grandmother would call, "Come in, my dear," but now all she heard was a grunt.

She opened the door.

Her grandmother looked even fatter than usual. And there was something else odd about her.

"Why, Granny," cried Little Red Riding Pig in amazement, "you have grown a long grey beard!"

But it was only the wolf's tail, still sticking out of her grandmother's mouth.

Miss Stevens, The Pig-Faced Lady

When Queen Victoria was crowned (1837), there was a great fair in Hyde Park. One of the sideshows at the fair was the Pig-Faced Lady.

Thousands of people came to gawp at this strange-looking person, who sat in a chair, wearing a long dress. Over her shoulders was a shawl, on her head a poke-bonnet, and on her hands white gloves.

Little did the onlookers know that the Pig-Faced Lady was in fact a brown bear.

The showman had had the hair shaved from the bear's face so that the white skin beneath looked like human flesh, and he had stuffed the fingers of the white gloves and fitted them over the animal's paws.

In addition, the bear was strapped tightly into the chair so that it could not move.

Ace, the popular television pigsonality, was appalled when we spoke to him about the Pig-Faced Lady:

But there's worse to come.

Behind the bear a boy was hidden, and each time the showman asked a question like, "I believe you are eighteen years old, Miss Stevens?" the boy gave the bear a poke in the back with a stick, and the bear gave a grunt.

"She understands perfectly," the showman would say to the crowd, "but she cannot answer properly because of the strange shape of her jaws."

Poor old bear.

I can't bear to think of it

hog wild!

David Mercer was a chubby child who soon earned the nickname 'Porker'. But even he's surprised at where his porky start in life has led him...

After a successful career as a lawyer David was looking for something a little different. He found it when he came up with the idea of a pig emporium, a shop specialising in everything to do with pigs. He set up *Hog Wild!* in 1978 in the famous Faneuil Hall Market in Boston, Massachusetts and proceeded to cram the shop with every conceivable item of porkophilia he could find, from piggy hot-water bottles, masks, slippers and jewellery to copper weather vanes!

Hog Wild! may have been the first speciality pig shop but its example was swiftly followed all over the States. Hog shops sprang up everywhere, including the outrageous *Hog Heaven* in North Little Rock, Arkansas – a shop selling paraphernalia for only one breed of pig.

Today *Hog Wild!* is the only surviving pig speciality shop in the States and it has beaten off all competitors with a massive mail order business, supplying hog merchandise to the whole country. Which all goes to prove that some Americans aren't just hog wild, they're hog crazy!

PIGGY BANKS

Vietnamese Pot-Bellied Pig

Perhaps the oddest looking of
all domestic pigs is the Vietnamese Pot-Bellied. It certainly
lives up to its name.
It's very fat, so fat that its stomach nearly brushes the ground. In fact, in the case of a
pregnant sow, it does, making walking very difficult. And because the pig's legs are so short
and its neck so plump, the Pot-Bellied has to have a flat pan rather than a trough for food and water.
There are two sizes of Pot-Bellied pigs – large and small – and two different types – one that is very docile
and tame, and one that is rather wild. Usually they are blackish in colour, but white or bluish ones are found,
though these may not be purebred, I'm not sure.
They like quite a bit of roughage in their diet, such as rolled barley, but of course, like all pigs, they will eat anything
and everything.
Pot-Bellied pigs were originally bought by Western sailors in the East for use as food while on board ship, and the story
goes that all the Vietnamese Pot-Bellied pigs born in Britain are descended from one brought home as a pet by a naval
officer some thirty years ago.
Lately a craze has developed – first in America and then in Britain – for keeping Pot-Bellied pigs as household pets; the pig
shares the kitchen or living room with its owners. (It is perfectly possible to house-train a pig, the cleanest of animals, as it
will never 'foul its own nest'.)
Personally I strongly disapprove of this because, as with all those unfortunate puppies bought on impulse at Christmas
and then discarded, some owners of Pot-Bellied pigs tend to get fed up with having them under their feet or just
can't manage them in the house, and the stories usually have unhappy endings.
But there's no doubt that if you have proper accommodation for one, and a paddock or orchard where it can
roam, a Vietnamese Pot-Bellied pig (one of the smaller, and more docile kind!) would make a most
endearing pet. No one could look at one of these tubs of lard without smiling. They really are
the strangest creatures.
But then the countries in the East seem to produce some very unusual pigs.
The latest breed to be imported, called the Meerschaum,
gives birth to twenty piglets at a go!

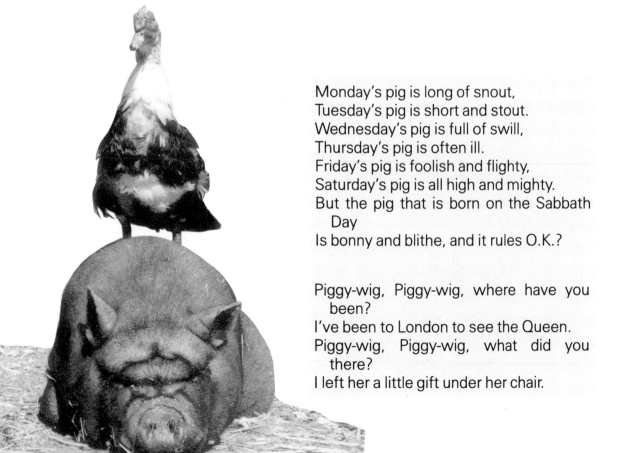

Monday's pig is long of snout,
Tuesday's pig is short and stout.
Wednesday's pig is full of swill,
Thursday's pig is often ill.
Friday's pig is foolish and flighty,
Saturday's pig is all high and mighty.
But the pig that is born on the Sabbath
Day
Is bonny and blithe, and it rules O.K.?

Piggy-wig, Piggy-wig, where have you
been?
I've been to London to see the Queen.
Piggy-wig, Piggy-wig, what did you
there?
I left her a little gift under her chair.

PARTY GUZZLES

Here are some suggestions of things to eat.
See if you can think of others...

PIGZA PERFECT (*well, they are!*)

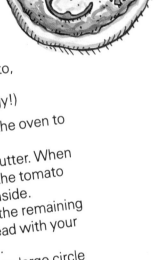

You will need:

300 g (12 oz) self-raising flour
150 ml (6 fl oz) milk
80 g (3½ oz) butter
Pinch of salt (optional)
150 g (6 oz) tomato puree
1 small onion, finely chopped
35 ml (1½ fl oz) water
½ teaspoon oregano
125 g (5 oz) grated cheese
Vegetables to decorate
(e.g. slices of green pepper, tomato,
mushroom and pepperoni)
(serves 6, or 4 if you're really piggy!)

Grease and flour a baking tray. Preheat the oven to
400°F/200°C/Gas Mark 6.
Fry the onion gently with a little of the butter. When
soft, remove from heat and mix with the tomato
puree, water and oregano. Set aside.
Now add the salt to the flour and rub in the remaining
butter evenly. Pour in the milk and knead with your
fingers into a smooth ball.
Roll out on a floured surface to form one large circle
(or two smaller circles, or even lots of little circles)
of dough.
Place the circle of dough on the baking tray and
spread the tomato mixture over the surface. Then
sprinkle with grated cheese. This is your pizza base –
now comes the fun bit!
Make a pig face with the slices of pepperoni,
mushroom, green pepper (for the mouth)
and tomato.
Bake in the middle of the oven for 20 minutes and
you'll have a perfect pigza!

TRIFFIC'S TROUGH SPECIAL

You will need:

75 g (3 oz) plain chocolate
3 eggs
3 tablespoons castor sugar
Fruit to decorate (e.g. banana,
kiwi fruit, apple)
(serves 4)

Break up the chocolate into small pieces and melt by placing it in a small bowl over a pan of simmering water. Do not allow the chocolate to boil or burn! Ask an adult to help you with this part of the recipe.
While the chocolate is melting, separate the eggs into yolks and whites. You may have to ask an adult to help you with this, too.
Beat the egg yolks lightly with a fork.
When the chocolate has melted, remove from heat, add the egg yolks and mix well.
Leave the mixture to cool (about 10 minutes).
Then, whisk the egg whites to form stiff peaks. Add half the sugar and whisk till the mixture is stiff again. Then add the rest of the sugar and whisk one last time.
Add the sugar and egg white mixture to the chocolate mixture, stirring gently.
Spoon into dessert glasses or bowls and chill in the fridge.
When your Trough Special has chilled (about 1 hour), decorate the top with slices and chunks of fruit – see if you can make a pig face!

PINK PIGGY POTION

You will need:

1 teaspoon strawberry syrup/sauce/
milk shake flavouring
1 small banana
1 scoop vanilla or strawberry ice cream
200 ml (8 fl oz) milk
Fruit to decorate (e.g. per glass: 2 half
slices of orange, a piece of orange peel,
2 glacé cherries, 1 slice of kiwi fruit)
(serves 1-2)

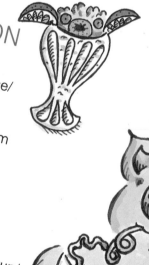

Peel banana and chop it into chunks.
Put the chopped banana, milk, ice cream and syrup/ sauce/flavouring into a blender or liquidizer and mix until frothy.
Pour the pink potion into a tall glass.
Decorate the rim of the glass with your fruit to make a piggy face (orange for ears, peel for tail, cherries for eyes, kiwi fruit for snout).
Now drink it with a straw. It's Ace!

MAKE YOUR OWN PIGGY BANK

You can make a piggy bank from recycled material – for yourself, or as a triffic gift.

You will need:

1 large cleaned-out plastic bottle
with cap (e.g. a fizzy drinks bottle)
2 used corks or cotton reels
Scraps of coloured paper or
fabric (e.g. felt)
1 pipe cleaner
Scissors
Glue

Ask an adult to help you make a slit on one side of the bottle (big enough for coins to drop through), and two holes on the other side, at either end of the bottle (large enough for your reels or corks to fit into snugly), for the piggy's feet. Use the fabric or paper to make eyes and ears, and some nostrils for the snout, and stick them to the bottle and bottle cap, as shown.

Curl the pipe cleaner around a pencil and attach to the pig's rear end as a curly tail.

Push your two reels or corks into their holes. Happy saving!

(To get your money you only have to unscrew the cap and out it comes!)

BOAR'S BRISTLES

If you have a boiled egg for breakfast why not save the shell and grow some boar's bristles?

Scoop out any remaining egg and carefully rinse out the empty shell.

Using crayons, pencils or felt-tip pens, draw a pig's mouth, snout and eyes on to the shell.

Cut out and glue on some paper ears and a paper tail (curled by wrapping the paper round a pencil).

Then fill the shell with damp cotton wool or scrunched-up kitchen paper.

Place the eggshell upright in an egg cup or empty egg carton.

Scatter cress seeds over the surface, to make an even but not too thick covering.

Stand the egg cup or carton on a sunny windowsill and leave it for 15-20 days.

Keep the shell covered with paper until the seeds have started to grow and water regularly so that the paper/cotton wool is always damp.

And hopefully, if you keep your trotters crossed, your piggy egg will sprout some bristles!

TRIFFIC

Chapter 4

Mules Can't

The Manager knew that a great many of the visitors to the Survival Centre were children, either with their parents or in a school party. He knew also that most children love animals, especially a baby animal such as a piglet, and particularly, without doubt, a small ginger piglet that, of all unlikely things, had struck up a friendship with a large grey mule. Already he had high hopes of Triffic as a crowd-puller. He needed to pull in the crowds to get money for his work of saving Rare Breeds.

"Joe," he said to the pigman next day, "I want you to let that little Tamworth gilt out, every morning, as soon as there are enough visitors around, understand?"

"Yes, Boss," said the pigman, puzzled.

Little madam of a pig, he thought, what's going on?

And to the stockman the Manager said, "I want Octavius exercised, Jim, every morning, as soon as there are enough visitors around, understand?"

"Yes, Boss," said the stockman, stumped.

Crabby old cuss of a mule, he thought, what's going on?

The sows too wondered what was going on.

Gradually, as the days went by, Teresa grew accustomed to Triffic's little outings and no longer took her to task. In fact she began to feel rather proud that a child of hers should be allowed a privilege that was denied to all other piglets.

But the rest were none too pleased, particularly when they learned the truth of the matter from the gossiping pigeons.

"Walking round the yard with a *mule*!" grunted Molly Middle-White.

"A mule!" sniffed Laetitia Large-Black. "The *lowest* form of animal life!"

"And attracting *crowds* of people!" grumbled Sarah Saddleback.

"Who should be down here admiring *our* children!" growled Glossy Old-Spots.

Even Betty Berkshire, closer to Teresa than the others, could not content herself with a mere snort but must needs comment directly. She looked over the wall one day, when the pigman had just let Triffic back into the sty, and shook her head disapprovingly.

"Naughty little girl!" she said.

Teresa bristled.

"Are you addressing my daughter, Mrs Berkshire?" she said.

"I am," said Betty. "You'll forgive me for saying so, Teresa, speaking as a much older sow, but you are allowing the child to make an exhibition of herself."

"You should just have heard my mum!" said Triffic to Octavius next morning. "'No, Mrs Berkshire,' she said. 'I will not forgive you, and I'll thank you to mind your own pigginess and keep your snout out of mine.' You should have seen the expression on Auntie Betty's face, Octavius! She was gobsmacked!"

"Your mother sounds a spirited person, young miss," said Octavius.

They were walking round the yard together, the stockman leading the mule and the piglet trotting beside, as the crowd of onlookers oohed and aahed at the sight of the odd couple.

"She is also very fortunate," went on Octavius, "to have such a daughter," and he sighed deeply.

"Have you never had a daughter then?" said Triffic.

"No."

"Only sons?"

"No."

"No children at all?"

"No," said Octavius in his customary tones of deepest gloom. "Mules can't."

"Can't have children of their own?" said Triffic. "Not ever?"

"That's right."

They went on in silence for a while. Then Octavius said, "It used not to bother me, but since meeting you, young miss, I have often wished that I could have had a child of my own."

Poor old chap, thought Triffic, and then she had an idea.

"Tell you what," she said. "I haven't got a father — at least I have, but not here, I've never seen him. He lives at another Survival Centre, Mum told me — she went over there for the wedding. So you could be my adopted father, Octavius. Then you'd have a daughter as well as a friend."

Octavius stopped abruptly in his tracks and stood stock-still. Unbreakably stubborn like all his kind, he took no notice of the stockman's efforts to haul him forward again, but with a sudden jerk of his head twitched the end of the halter-rope from the man's hands.

"Young miss," he said, "you have just made an old mule very happy. They named you well when they called you Triffic."

At these words Triffic also felt very happy. Without really thinking what she was doing, she took the end of the rope in her mouth and walked on. Octavius followed.

"Look at that!" cried somebody in the crowd of watching visitors, and everyone, the children especially, looked and pointed and laughed and cheered at the amazing sight of a very old grey mule being led around the cobbled yard of the Survival Centre by a very young ginger piglet.

The pigman came up to see what all the noise was about, and stood beside the stockman.

"Did you ever, Jim?" he said.

"I never, Joe," said the stockman, and they took off their greasy old caps and scratched their heads.

Next morning the Manager, forewarned by his men, came to watch.

He stood beside Joe and saw Jim drop the rope and the piglet once again pick up the end of it and walk on. He listened to the delighted comments of the day's visitors.

"What a wonderful pair!" they said, and, "It's better than a circus!" and, "Ought to be on the telly, they did!" and he stroked his beard and smiled behind his hand.

"You know what, Joe?" he said to the pigman. "She's terrific, she is!"

The weeks passed, weeks in which larger and larger numbers of people came to visit the Centre, to see now, in addition to all the Rare Breeds of cattle and horses and sheep and pigs and goats and poultry, the daily show put on in the great yard by old Octavius and his little friend.

36

By now the act was improved, thanks to an idea of the Manager's.

Experimenting with the pair one evening after the public had gone home, he found that when he ordered Octavius to stop, the piglet had perforce to do so also, since patently she could not tow the mule forward: and when he told Octavius to go on again, so must Triffic or risk being stepped on.

So now to the visitors' delight the word "Whoa!" brought both to a halt, and then away they both went again at the command "Walk on!"

"What was all that noise I heard just now?" said Teresa when Triffic returned after the first demonstration of these new skills.

"That was the people, Mum," said Triffic. "They were cheering Octavius and me like anything, can't think why. Funny creatures, people. Make an awful row about nothing, they do, just like my brothers."

She looked round the outer part of the sty.

"By the way, where are they?" she said. "All asleep inside?"

"No," said Teresa. "They've gone."

"Gone? Where?"

"I don't know," said Teresa (who didn't).

Next door Betty Berkshire (who did) gave a loud snort. She said nothing however, since she and Teresa were still not on speaking terms.

The pigman came in with a bucket and filled the trough.

"There you are, old lady, eat up and get your strength back, got to have you in good condition ready for the next lot," he said. "And as for you, little madam, you're on your own now. I expect you'll miss your brothers, eh?"

"What's he on about, Mum?" said Triffic.

"Haven't a clue," said Teresa. "I expect you'll miss your brothers, eh?"

"You must be joking, Mum," said Triffic with her mouth full. "There's no one to hog my grub any more."

continued on page 46

HOGS IN AMERICA

In Great Britain a hog is a male pig – but in America all pigs are called hogs.

Twenty per cent of all the corn grown in America is fed to hogs, and hog-raising (what we should call pig-farming) is concentrated in the Corn Belt States. These are: Illinois, Indiana, Iowa, Minnesota, Missouri, Nebraska and Ohio. Iowa has the largest hog population – 14,800,000 animals.

You might be forgiven for thinking, from figures like that, that there are more pigs (sorry, hogs) in America than anywhere else in the world. Not so. America only comes third. Second is Russia, and first, with forty per cent of all the pigs kept, is China.

The eight commonest breeds of hog in the USA are: the American Landrace, the Chester White (a fair-skinned hog, liable to sunburn and thus needing shade), the Duroc, the Hampshire (a breed marked like our Wessex Saddleback), the Poland-China, the Spotted Swine, and two breeds that were imported from Great Britain in the 1800s, the Berkshire and the Yorkshire.

Just in case you can't guess how many hogs (sorry, pigs) there are on this planet, I'll tell you.

Seven hundred and sixty million – that's 760,000,000!

The Owl and the Pussy-cat

You all know that the Owl and the Pussy-cat went to sea in a beautiful pea-green boat. But do you remember the Piggy-wig they met in a wood with a ring at the end of his nose? And do you ever wonder what he did with the shilling that they gave him? Well, read on...

Said the Piggy, "I Will"

"At last," said the Piggy-wig, "I can rootle!"

Rootling in the ground with their strong snouts is something all pigs love doing, but they cannot rootle if they have rings in their noses.

"At last," said the Piggy-wig again, "I am rid of that horrid ring. And what's more, that Owl and that Pussy-cat actually paid me for it! A whole shilling! Though I do not know what on earth to do with it. But talking of earth gives me an idea," and he dug a little hole with his snout and buried the shilling in a safe place, under the Bong-tree. Then off he went all around the wood, rootling and rootling to his heart's content.

He had turned up all sorts of nice things – bulbs and roots and beetles – when suddenly his snout struck upon something hard. It was a large spoon, whose handle had been bent at right angles to its bowl by the force of the pig's rootling.

At that moment the Turkey who lives on the hill came strutting by.

"That spoon won't be much use to you at the wedding-feast," he said.

"I haven't been asked," said the pig.

"Pity," said the turkey. "They're having mince. And slices of quince."

The pig licked his lips.

"I could get you an invite," said the turkey.

"Could you?" said the pig eagerly.

"At a price."

"How much?"

"One shilling."

"Done!" said the pig, and he rushed back to the Bong-tree and dug up his shilling and gave it to the turkey.

Next day the Owl and the Pussy-cat were married by the Turkey who lives on the hill. All the invited guests (including the pig) were there, and all had brought wedding presents (except the pig).

"What can I give them?" he whispered anxiously to the turkey, who sniggered and replied, "Give 'em that old spoon."

Quickly, for he did not want to miss the wedding-feast, the pig ran back to the wood and found the spoon.

When he returned with it, he could see that something was wrong.

The Pussy-cat was in tears, the Owl was trying to comfort her, and the guests were tut-tutting and dear-dearing among themselves.

"All ruined!" cried the Pussy-cat. "All wasted!"

"O lovely Pussy!" said the Owl. "Whatever's the matter?"

"Mince!" cried the Pussy-cat. "And slices of quince! There's only one possible way to eat them and that we cannot do!"

At this moment the Piggy-wig pushed his way through the crowd of guests, and dropped before the unhappy couple the large spoon with the right-angled handle.

"Hope you'll be very happy," he said gruffly.

"O Piggy-wig!" cried the Pussy-cat, drying her tears. "Now we most certainly shall be! Your wedding present is the one thing that we needed, the one thing without which it is not possible to dine on mince, and slices of quince!"

"O Pussy my love!" said the Owl, looking in puzzlement at the Piggy-wig's present. "What is it?"

"You elegant fowl!" laughed the Pussy-cat joyfully. "It's a runcible spoon!"

The Piglet's Crusade

Said a pig to his mother, "I'm terribly keen
To travel to London to talk to the Queen.
I need to consult her, while paying a visit,
About my idea." Said his mother, "What is it?"
"It's this," said the piglet. "As I understand,
Men, women and children all over the land
Eat bits of the pig as a part of their diet?"
"You're right," said his mother. "I cannot deny it."
"Suppose," said the piglet, "The Queen should proclaim
With all the authority due to her name
That anyone eating a pig was a sinner?
Why, nobody ever would have us for dinner
Or breakfast or luncheon or afternoon tea,
If it was forbidden by Royal Decree."
"You've got to be joking, my boy. Pull the other
One – it's got the bells on it," snorted his mother.
"You talk to the Queen? How d'you get to her? Fly?"
"Pigs can't," said her son, "but I'm going. Goodbye."
And happily humming a popular ditty
Set off on the road to the capital city.

Arriving in London, his trotters quite sore
From pounding the shoulder along the M4,
Amazed at the number of streets and the thunder
Of traffic, the piglet stood gaping in wonder,
Till after a while a policeman drew near
And said to the runaway, "What's all this 'ere?"
In tones that were friendly and quite without malice.
"Which way," said the piglet, "to Buckingham Palace?"
"I'll tell you, me lad," the policeman replied,
"But don't you go thinking they'll let you inside.
'Er Majesty's usual orders, of course, is
'No animals in 'ere but corgis and 'orses'."

Indeed, when the piglet walked into the yard,
The sentry on duty bawled, "Turn out the guard!"
And guardsmen came rushing from every quarter
Intent, so it seemed to the piglet, on slaughter.
At sight of the soldiers he took to his heels
And ran through their legs with a volley of squeals.
Straight in through the door of the Palace he scurried
And up a great carpeted staircase he hurried.
Through corridors, passages, hallways he tore
Until by good fortune he chanced on a door
On which was a notice. QUEEN ONLY, it stated.
I've found her at last, thought the piglet, elated,

And then – nothing venture, they say, nothing win –
He knocked on the door and a voice said, "Come in."
Obeying this order, he found the Queen sitting
Surrounded by corgis and doing some knitting.
The corgis all barked and the Queen said, "Tut! Tut!
Shut up, do you hear me?" and up they all shut.
"And now," said the Queen, "what's the matter, young shaver?"
"I've come," said the piglet, "to ask you a favour,
Your Majesty, if you'll allow me to speak."
"A piglet addressing a Queen! What a cheek!"
The Monarch replied, but she couldn't help smiling –
The piglet was looking so cute and beguiling.
"Go on. Ask your favour then. What's all the fuss?"
"Please, Ma'am," said the piglet, "please stop eating us."

"What's that?" said the Queen. "If we're not much mistaken,
"You're asking us if we will stop eating bacon
And sausage and ham and pigs' trotters and pork –
Prince Philip and me and the Duchess of York
And Princess Diana and all of the others,
My sister, my mummy, and Charles and his brothers.
Is that what you're asking?" The piglet said, "Yes.
That's just the idea that I came to express.
I truly and earnestly hope to inveigle
Your Majesty into declaring illegal

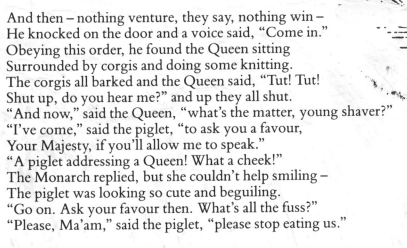

The eating of pig-meat of every sort.
It's only the Queen that can do it, I thought.
If she should forbid it, then no one would risk it."
"I must say," the Queen said, "you do take the biscuit!
I certainly see you'd be filled with relief
If I were to legislate 'Let them eat beef'
Or chicken or turkey or mutton or lamb
But never pork sausages, bacon or ham.
For you and your lot that would be the solution.
For me, it would certainly mean revolution!
They'd take off my crown and, quite likely, my head.
I'd sooner eat pig-meat than finish up dead."

So glum did the piglet appear when she'd spoken –
His mission a failure, his heart all but broken –
That quickly the Queen added, "Do stay to tea –
It's only the corgis and Philip and me –
And how would you like (for with you I've no quarrel)
To live out the rest of your days at Balmoral?"
And that is the tale of the piglet that met
The Queen and remained as Her Majesty's pet.
Though in his crusade for his kind he was beaten,
By Royal Decree he could never be eaten
But lived his long life in a fine Scottish sty –
The apple of good Queen Elizabeth's eye.

PIGGY BANKS

Have you ever wondered why we save our money in a china, pottery, or even a plastic pig, rather than in some other animal? Well, read on...

The first piggy banks we know about were made in the twelfth and thirteenth centuries in China and South-East Asia, in places where owning a pig was a symbol of wealth. A pottery pig would be made as an offering for a funeral and stuffed with paper money, specially made for the occasion. It is thought that this was a gift to the dead person, to help send the soul on its way. By the seventeenth century the idea of piggy banks had spread to Western and Northern Europe. People in many European countries saw the pig as a symbol of thrift and good fortune. That's probably the reason why piggy banks are still so popular today.

GROOMING FOR PIGS
Tip No. 2
Beauty Oil for the Show Pig

Never go to an agricultural show unless you are well oiled. Pure olive oil is expensive, so reserve this for the best shows of the lot: the Royal and the Bath & West. For lesser shows you will find corn oil or a cheap supermarket vegetable oil quite satisfactory.

For those among family or friends not good enough to accompany you to the show ring, remember, before you leave, to remind them of the old saying, "If you can't join 'em, lick 'em." This will remove any surplus from your coat.

The first pig I ever owned was a Large White sow called Carnera. Carnera had a special trick – she loved to escape.

Freedom was what she craved, and she hated to be confined in any way – in a sty, in a pen, in a yard, in a paddock or even in a whopping great field. Somehow or other she would manage to break down a door or burst through a fence or hedge, and she would even get her snout under a length of pig-wire and uproot it, posts and all.

Then Carnera would go galloping off into the wild blue yonder, grinning all over her great fat face.

Then one day I saw in a farming magazine an advertisement which said:

PIG-PROOF HARNESS

Calling all pig farmers! Fit our patent pig-proof harness and your fencing problems will be over. This equipment is made from the finest materials and is guaranteed to restrain the strongest of pigs. Simply fit the harness (adjustable to any size of adult animal), attach restraining spring and chain to anchor-stake, and your pig is safely tethered, wherever you wish.

It was very expensive but no matter, I thought. No more worries about Carnera escaping.

Strangely enough she didn't seem to mind (maybe because she had her snout deep in a trough full of food) as I adjusted the complex web of stout leather straps around her huge body, and fastened the buckles, and connected the harness to the enormous spring, and the spring to the long steel chain, and the chain to the heavy anchor-stake which I'd driven deep into the ground with a sledge-hammer.

"Gotcha, Carnera!" I said, and stood back to watch.

Carnera finished her grub and walked off. She walked until she came to the limit of the thirty-foot chain, and this brought her up short.

She grunted angrily and strained onward. The enormous spring expanded a little but that was all.

Carnera gave a squeal of fury and lunged forward again.

Once more the spring expanded but the pig was firmly held, no doubt about it.

Carnera squealed louder.

"You're wasting your breath," I shouted. "This contraption would hold an elephant."

Hardly had the words left my mouth than Carnera drew back a few paces and then, with a final volley of squeals, threw herself forward.

The heavy anchor-stake stood firm. The long steel chain, though taut and vibrating, and the enormous spring, though expanded to its full extent, took the strain.

Then suddenly with a clap of sound like a salvo of gunfire the stout leather straps of the pig-proof harness burst asunder as though they were merely string, and once again Carnera went galloping off into the wild blue yonder, grinning all over her great fat face.

THE WILD BOAR

This bristly pig comes in a variety of colours – reddish, brown, chocolate or black. It is found in Europe, Africa, India and China. Its bite, which is a ripping rather than a slicing action, is said to be worse than that of any mammal except the Killer Whale.

THE WARTHOG

This is a ridiculous-looking African animal with skinny legs and a huge head. It has grotesque warts on the sides of its face, and an absurd skinny tail like a lavatory-brush which it holds straight up as it trots along. Its tusks grow first outwards, then upwards, and finally inwards. It lives in a large hole into which it always goes backwards.

THE PECCARY

Peccaries live mainly in South America. They can be extremely dangerous to other animals, silently surrounding their chosen prey and then closing in on it. At other times they clap their jaws together when angry, and this is a severe warning to all creatures (including man) to stay at a safe distance.

THE PIGMY PIG

Adult Pigmy Pigs, which live in the hill forests of the Himalayas, stand only a foot high at the shoulder. The piglets, striped brown and yellow, are only the size of a small bar of chocolate when born.

Y SWINE

THE BEARDED PIG
This is the largest known swine, measuring over six feet in length. It has a huge crested head and a bristly moustache.

THE FOREST HOG
No one knows much about this animal, except that it can be almost as big as the Bearded Pig. It lives in Africa.

THE AFRICAN BUSH PIG
These pigs have long pointed ears ending in plumes of hair and long hairy tails. They are the best of all pigs at rooting, turning the forest floor upside down. Working together in teams of up to fifty, they can even move the fallen trunks of very large trees.

THE BABIRUSA
Babirusas live in the East Indies. They have four tusks which stick up in front of their faces. They rootle about in swamps by night, and are extremely timid. They are very good to eat.

TRIFFIC

Chapter 5

She's Moved House

Leading Octavius around the yard and stopping and starting on command were soon not the only tricks in Triffic's repertoire.

All pigs are intelligent and Triffic, it seemed, was especially so for she quickly learned a number of other bits of business which the Manager thought up to amuse the public.

All of them demanded the co-operation of Octavius, hitherto the most unco-operative animal anyone could imagine, but now, to the stockman's great surprise, eager to please.

He stood still when told, for example, and let the piglet walk between his legs. He lay down flat on his side so that she could play King of the Castle upon his stomach. He even allowed himself to be harnessed to a kind of sledge, upon which the Manager trained Triffic to stand, and pulled her along behind him. And all this the old mule did willingly, with never even the threat of the biting and kicking that once was his stock-in-trade.

"Can't understand it, Boss," the stockman said. "No one would ever believe what a crabby old cuss he was. He's a changed animal."

The Manager nodded. He understood Octavius's altered state only too well, and he blamed himself fairly and squarely for having allowed the animal to be tied up in a dark stable all this time, as though he was some sort of pariah. At least this state of affairs had been put right. The old mule had been moved to a fine roomy loose-box whose door bore a notice saying simply:

> OCTAVIUS
> The sole survivor of
> an eight-mule team

And now thanks to Triffic, Octavius had not only a friend (an adopted daughter you might say, the Manager caught himself thinking, smiling at the absurdity of such a notion) but also the daily admiration, adulation indeed, of the crowds who came to watch and applaud the increasingly famous pig-and-mule act. Such was the demand for it that there were now two performances each morning and two each afternoon.

Triffic worried a bit about this.

"Octavius," she said.

"Yes, my dear?"

"You're sure it's not too much for you? Four shows a day, I mean — it's a lot of walking and pulling that sledge and everything. After all, you're not as young as you were."

"On the contrary, my dear," replied Octavius, "I am younger than I was, much younger — in spirit, that is. They feed me better, indeed I even get a ration of oats now, I have a large well-lit new home with room to roll and stretch out comfortably in the straw, I have all the fresh air and exercise that I lacked before, and, to be frank, I must confess that I derive a good deal of enjoyment from performing our little shows, as you call them. It is most pleasant, I find, to be the centre of attention, clapped and cheered by the people. It has taken years off me. And it is all thanks to you, my dear."

Triffic was quite reassured by this long speech from her adopted father, which she later reported to her natural mother.

"He's so much happier, Mum," she said, "you wouldn't believe."

"I am glad for him," said Teresa. "And I am glad for you, child, that you seem to have this gift of spreading happiness. Why, the fantail pigeons tell me that you are given a welcome wherever you go in the Centre — from the biggest Longhorn bull to the smallest bantam hen. Certainly my neighbours have nothing but good to say of you now."

This change of heart on behalf of the other sows was easily explained. Each time that Triffic finished her act and ran home, a great many of the visitors, the children especially, followed her down to the line of pigsties, and so paid far more attention than ever before to the rest of the Rare mother and baby pigs.

"You'd never think to look at them," people said, staring down at the sows and their litters,

"that they were so intelligent. But they must be — just look what that little ginger one has learned to do."

"You'd never think to look at them," grunted Molly Middle-White, staring up at the people, "that they had much in the way of brains. But they must have — just look at them admiring our children."

"They follow that Triffic Tamworth down here, I notice," said Laetitia Large-Black.

"That's true," said Sarah Saddleback. "She seems to attract them in this direction."

"At least she's making herself useful," said Glossy Old-Spots.

"Maybe we misjudged her," said Betty Berkshire. She looked over the wall and nodded her head approvingly.

"Good little girl!" she said.

"Who, me, Auntie Betty?" said Triffic.

"Yes, you, dear."

"I'm glad that you seem to approve of my daughter now, Betty," said Teresa drily.

"Oh yes," said Betty Berkshire. "Let bygones be bygones, that's my motto. Life's too short."

Or it is for some pigs, she thought. Thank goodness I was born a female and of a Rare Breed.

"I expect it's quite a relief to be rid of your hogs, Teresa," she said. "A first litter is always tiring. And the way time flies, you'll be hearing the patter of tiny trotters again before you can

look round. You'll be wanting young Triffic out of the way then."

"She's welcome to stay as long as she likes," said Teresa Tamworth.

Triffic saw her opportunity. For some time now she had been growing impatient of her dependence upon the pigman coming to let her out or in, and of her imprisonment in the sty at times when she was not performing. What she wanted was total freedom to go wherever she liked whenever she liked within the Rare Breeds Survival Centre. More, she fancied sharing Octavius's loose-box — an easy matter since the stockman had fixed rails across the front of it upon which the public could lean to look at the mule and under which Triffic could easily go.

"Mum," she said now. "Would you mind awfully if I moved in with my friend Octavius?"

Teresa hesitated. She was fond of this child, her first and so far only daughter, but she was aware that, as Betty said, there would be other daughters and sons before too long. Besides, some instinct told her that Triffic was a very special individual, destined for great things, so at length she answered her question quite simply.

"Of course not, my love," she said. "You go and keep your old mule company. But come back for a chat now and again, won't you?"

"Oh yes," said Betty. "You must come and see us all. You're such a crowd-puller, you know."

"I will!" said Triffic. "Every day."

Later, after the second afternoon performance, the pigman had finished feeding the sows and was leaning on Teresa's door, waiting for Triffic.

"Where's that little madam got to then, old lady?" he said when the piglet did not appear, but Teresa only grunted. So the pigman walked up the yard till he saw the stockman coming out of Octavius's loose-box.

"Seen my Tamworth gilt, Jim?" he said.

"That I have, Joe," said the stockman, and he jerked his thumb over his shoulder.

"Take a look," he said.

The pigman took it. There was Octavius lying comfortably in his deep bed of straw, and beside him lay Triffic.

She jumped up when she saw the pigman and let out a string of little snorts and squeaks that said plainly, "I'm hungry, you stupid fellow, so kindly fetch a trough and some food to put in it, and look sharp!"

When the pigman had obeyed — for even he could not misinterpret this message — he and the stockman leaned upon the rails, elbows on the upper one, a foot each on the lower, and stared thoughtfully at the odd couple. They did not take off their greasy old caps to scratch their heads, because by now they were thoroughly used to the partnership, and both knew, for the Manager had told them, how important it had become. Never had the takings been so good, especially since the media had cottoned on to the double act and given the Centre so much publicity.

Only recently a television crew had come to record the latest trick which the Manager had devised.

He fitted Octavius, harnessed to the sledge, with a set of reins, and those parts which a human driver would normally have held he coated with treacle. Then he trained Triffic to hold them in her mouth. This, having a lot of very sweet teeth, she willingly did, and the nation's TV screens showed the astounding sight of a piglet not merely being pulled along by a mule, but actually driving one.

"Reckon she's moved house then, Jim," said the pigman. Little madam, he was about to say but somehow that no longer seemed right.

"Little marvel!" he said.

"Reckon you're right, Joe," said the stockman. "The old mule won't half be pleased, though you'd never think so to look at him." Crabby old cuss, he was about to add but somehow that no longer seemed right.

"Funny old codger!" he said.

The little marvel and the funny old codger settled down most happily together. Octavius was never now lonely for one moment, and as for Triffic, though she liked to potter about all over the Centre, chatting to this animal and that, and never forgetting regular visits to her mother and her aunties, she most looked forward to the end of the working day. Then she could settle down in the loose-box and listen to all the tales that Octavius had to tell, of the days of long ago.

He spoke of his father the donkey and his mother the mare, and of his seven mates in the eight-strong team. Primus, the eldest, had once been an army mule, carrying heavy machine-guns up Italian mountains, and Quartus and Quintus had worked in a circus, "but the best times, my dear," said Octavius, "was when all eight of us were employed together, here on the farm. Forget your Shire horses and your Percherons and your Suffolk Punches — there was no load so heavy that we lads couldn't shift it. What a bunch of boys we were. All gone now though, except me, and I dare say I shan't be long in following them."

"Oh rubbish, Octavius," said Triffic. "There's no danger of that."

But there was.

Late one afternoon, just before closing time, when the last of the day's visitors were leaving the Survival Centre, four people were still standing at the front of Octavius's loose-box. A man and a woman leaned on the top rail, their two children on the bottom, staring at the piglet and the mule.

The children were eating sweets, and the man was puffing a cigarette despite the NO SMOKING notice on the loose-box door as on every other door of the Centre, where so much hay and straw were stored.

They were not cruel people, just thoughtless, and the children chucked their sweet-papers and the bag that had held the toffees on the floor, despite the fact that one of the many bins labelled LITTER was handy.

"Time to go," said the man to his wife, and he took a final puff and dropped his fag-end, and off they all went.

The butt of the cigarette lay on the cobbles, still glowing. Then a little breeze blew in through the door and shifted the sweet-bag towards it. It caught alight.

The paper bag lay burning and might have burned out had not the little breeze blown in once more, and lifted it, and moved it, just a couple of feet.

But that was enough to drop it on to the edge of Octavius's straw bed.

continued on page 56

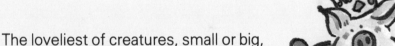

The loveliest of creatures, small or big,
Is, without any doubt at all, the Pig.

■

Speak not to me of the Impala's grace,
The Tiger's majesty, the Cheetah's pace.
Say naught about the great Gorilla's
    strength,

■

The Sable's coat, the
Anaconda's length.
Tell me no tales of Elephantine might,
Of Peacock's glory or of Eagle's flight.

■

Earth hath not anything to show more fine
Than that most beautiful of beasts,
the Swine.

Goldipig and the Three Bears

Goldipig was a very inquisitive little swine, always poking her snout into other people's business.

Rooting about in the forest one day, she came upon a house among the trees. "I wonder who lives there?" said Goldipig, and when she had called "Hullo!" and no one had answered, she pushed open the door and went in.

The first thing she saw was a table with three chairs around it, one big, one ordinary-sized, one little, and on the table, in front of each chair, was a bowl of porridge, one big, one ordinary-sized, one little.

Goldipig scoffed the lot.

Then, nosy as ever, she trotted upstairs. There in a bedroom were three beds, one big, one ordinary-sized, one little.

"I'll have a nap," said Goldipig, feeling rather full.

She tried each bed in turn. The first was too little, the second too ordinary, but the third, the big bed, was just right, so Goldipig snuggled down in it and went to sleep.

Shortly afterwards the owners of the house returned. They had been taking a walk to work up an appetite for breakfast. They were in fact three bears, one big, one ordinary-sized, one little.

"Who's been sitting on our chairs?" said the little bear.

"And where's our porridge gone?" said the ordinary-sized bear.

"And who," said the big bear, listening carefully, "is that snoring upstairs?"

Very quietly the three bears climbed to the bedroom and looked in and saw Goldipig.

"She's messed up all our beds," said the little bear

"After eating all our porridge," said the ordinary-sized bear.

"And so," said the big bear, "we'll jolly well eat her."

At that, Goldipig let out an enormous squeal, dashed past the bears and rushed downstairs and away. So you can see the three of them got neither porridge nor ham for their breakfast!

The Iron Age Pig

This is a 'manufactured' breed, the result of an experiment by farmer Joe Henson of the Cotswold Farm Park, a leading figure in the fight for the survival of rare breeds.

The idea was to try to establish a strain that would resemble as closely as possible the original Wild Boar which still exists on the European mainland and once roamed British forests.

A pure wild boar was lent by the London Zoo and was crossed with a Tamworth sow, the Tamworth being a hardy long-snouted breed most closely resembling the wild type.

The resulting stripey piglets were very similar to the domestic animals kept by Iron Age farmers. The stripes disappear with maturity, and the adult animal's coat is blackish.

Henson kept breeding these crosses together, choosing those most like the wild boar and also of a docile nature, and has sold a great many: the British population is now probably more than two hundred. The crossbred sows are tamer and more prolific than wild sows, and are now being mated to wild boars to produce wild boar meat which is much in demand.

The Monster in the Shed

Great oaks, they say, from little acorns grow and the largest pig I have ever seen was full of the things.

The year was 1943, the month September, and the Allied forces had not long landed at Salerno, in Southern Italy.

My platoon of the Grenadier Guards was dug in on the banks of a stream, near a farmyard from which the Italians had fled, taking all their livestock with them.

Except one.

Searching the buildings, I came upon a shed whose door was bolted. I could hear strange noises inside.

"There's someone in here," I whispered to the sergeant who was with me. "Might be Germans. Watch out. I'm going to open the door."

I did, and a great avalanche of acorns rolled out.

Inside the dark shed there was silence now but on top of a positive mountain of the things we could dimly see a monstrous shape.

"Come on out!" I shouted, and down from the top of the acorn mountain rushed the most enormous black bristly pig.

Out of the door it went and across the farmyard it went, but it didn't get far. That sergeant was a good shot.

What's more, if you can believe it (and you must, it's true) he had been a butcher in civilian life, and by the end of the day that pig was cut up and cooked, and thirty-five men had a wonderful feast.

I've eaten a lot of pig-meat since then, but never anything as good as acorn-fed Italian pork.

Saddlebottom, the famous mascot of the Wessex Rifles, comments:

Fancy soldiers making pigs of themselves!

PIG POTTERY

The Saltford Pottery near Bristol thrives on making and selling pottery pigs, in fact it's not so much a pottery as a piggery. Owner Charles Baker, his wife Robbie and their staff model a range of pottery pigs and piggy banks – many of them based on rare breeds such as Tamworths and Saddlebacks.

The pottery pigs sell especially well in Japan, Iceland and the US and potters from Saltford have travelled internationally demonstrating their skills and exhibiting their pigs. Sadly the pigs are now in such great demand that they can no longer be modelled individually and are made, instead, from moulds. But as a result of their success far more people are aware of the many rare breeds of pig in need of protection and the Saltford Pottery (itself a member of the Rare Breeds Survival Trust) has lent a helping trotter in the campaign to save rare breeds.

CHINESE CALENDAR

Do you have a Pig Personality?

Although much of the world celebrates New Year on January 1st, the Chinese New Year is moveable, beginning on a day in January or February. The date is determined by the position of the moon, and each year has a different animal sign, one of twelve. Chinese legend tells us that this came about as follows...

One Chinese New Year, more than five centuries before Christ, the prince Buddha requested all animals to journey to see him before his death. Twelve came to bid him farewell. In recognition Buddha gave each animal a year, in the order of their arrival. First was the Rat, then the Ox, the Tiger, Rabbit, Dragon, Snake, Horse, Goat (some refer to this as the Year of the Sheep), Monkey, Cock (or Rooster), Dog and Pig (or Boar). The twelve make up a cycle, so when one cycle is over, the next begins again, with the Rat.

The Chinese believe that the animal sign under which you are born influences your life and that some of your personality can be traced to your sign. Pigs are honest, brave and generous. They are tolerant and don't bear grudges – but are immensely self-centred.

Look at the chart below and work out your animal sign according to the Chinese Calender, and those of your family and friends. Try and find out the characteristics of the other signs – your local library will be able to help.

RAT		OX		TIGER		RABBIT		DRAGON		SNAKE	
1900	1948	1901	1949	1902	1950	1903	1951	1904	1952	1905	1953
1912	1960	1913	1961	1914	1962	1915	1963	1916	1964	1917	1965
1924	1972	1925	1973	1926	1974	1927	1975	1928	1976	1929	1977
1936	1984	1937	1985	1938	1986	1939	1987	1940	1988	1941	1989

HORSE		GOAT		MONKEY		COCK		DOG		PIG	
1906	1954	1907	1955	1908	1956	1909	1957	1910	1958	1911	1959
1918	1966	1919	1967	1920	1968	1921	1969	1922	1970	1923	1971
1930	1978	1931	1979	1932	1980	1933	1981	1934	1982	1935	1983
1942	1990	1943	1991	1944	1992	1945	1993	1946	1994	1947	1995

Happy Endings

Pigs are happiest (in my opinion) when allowed to live a life as nearly as possible like that of their wild ancestors.

For many years I kept a small herd of pigs in a wood. The wood was squarish in shape, and round it I built a wooden fence made from elm boards, topped with pig-wire. The elm boards were second-rate ones with knot holes or other faults in them, not suitable for their proper use – the making of coffins – but fine for keeping pigs from straying.

The herd was composed of ten Wessex Saddleback sows and a Large White boar.

The wood had grown up naturally on the site of an old open-cast coal mine, so the ground on which the many trees stood – ash mostly, with elder and holly and a fair number of oaks – was a mass of humps and deep hollows.

There were two small buildings in the wood – brick-built tin-roofed Nissen huts in which the local Home Guard had stored their ammunition during the Second World War – and if the weather was very bad, the pigs would shelter in these. But mostly they slept out, for the humps and hollows left by those old miners meant that they could always find shelter from a cold wind or shade from a hot sun, and in addition the soil was well-drained.

I fed them on pig-nuts, a specially balanced ration that contained all they needed, simply taking a bag of the stuff and hollering, "Pig-pig-pig-pig!" and tipping the nuts out in a long trail which the pigs followed.

But as well as eating what I gave them, they found a great deal of their food in the wood, just as their wild cousins would have done.

They turned up the ground with their strong snouts for roots and bulbs and fungi, and they ate the greenery – grass and bushes and the leaves of low branches – and in the autumn especially, when the oaks shed their acorns, the pigs had a bonanza.

There was even an old pond in the wood where they could wallow and coat themselves in a lovely gooey mudpack.

Usually when the sows were near to farrowing I would take them out of the wood to a paddock where there were huts in which they had their babies, but sometimes I wasn't quick enough.

I shall never forget one very frosty morning after a bitterly cold night, when I was hunting through the wood for one of the sows, called Sugar Ray Robinson (I called all my sows after professional boxers of that time).

I was afraid that I'd left things too late and that she had farrowed out in the open. My mind was full of visions of chilled or already dead piglets in such hard winter weather.

I needn't have worried.

Sugar Ray Robinson had built a huge nest, I found, a nest the size of a small room, made of dried grass and bracken and twigs and branches, in the deepest and most sheltered of all the hollows.

There was thick frost over most of the wood but none here, and she was perfectly protected from the wind. Most of the trees were bare of leaves of course, but not the great old yew that stood, like a giant umbrella, above the nest where the sow lay, nursing ten fat, dry, warm piglets.

I've never forgotten how happy Sugar Ray looked. Or how happy I felt as I went quietly off to fetch her some breakfast.

Q · How do you spot a pig who's a good actor?

A · It's playing Hamlet

Chapter 6

A Heroine

Those last four visitors (the man just lighting another cigarette) were in the act of walking out of the main gates of the Centre as the outer edge of Octavius's bed caught fire.

His day's work done, the pigman was having a last look down the line of sties, and the stockman, in the main stables, was giving a final friendly slap to the gleaming black backside of a great Shire stallion before knocking off.

In his office, the Manager stroked his beard contentedly as his secretary told him the total of the day's takings and as he converted, in his head, the sum of money into bales of hay and bags of concentrates to feed his beloved Rare Breeds.

Octavius was in the middle of a story about Secundus, the strongest mule of the team, who had once been hitched to a cow that had slipped into a deep ditch and had hauled her out by his own unaided efforts.

At that moment the flames took a proper hold of the thick dry straw, and rose in an almost solid wall along the line of the rails across the front of the loose-box.

"Quick!" groaned the old grey mule, backing hastily away from the blaze. "Get out while you can!"

Triffic dashed to safety beneath the bottom rail, at the far end, where the flames had not yet reached. She turned to see them reach it. There was a side-door to the loose-box, she knew, but it was bolted, and the mule was too big to get under or between the rails and too old and stiff to be able to jump out.

The first thought that Triffic had was to get help, and the last thing she heard, as she ran squealing at the top of her voice down the yard, was the frantic battering of Octavius's heels as he tried to kick down the rails.

The pigman heard the earsplitting non-stop row the piglet was making, and looked up, and saw the smoke. He grabbed a couple of buckets and ran for the water tank as fast as his bulk would allow.

The stockman too heard the noise and saw the smoke. He unreeled the stable hosepipe and ran for the loose-box as fast as his bow legs would let him.

Both men yelled "FIRE! FIRE!" and the Manager heard them from his office.

"Nine Nine Nine! Fire Brigade! Quick!" he snapped at his secretary, and he snatched an extinguisher off the wall.

He could hear the crackle of flames as he raced across the yard, and because he was fit and long-legged he arrived at the same time as his men. Flinging them the extinguisher, he dashed around to the side-door of the loose-box.

Triffic watched all this, her heart thudding madly. There was no sound from within now, nothing but the roar of the fire. A horse trapped thus would have been screaming, but a mule will bear terrible pain and make no sound. Triffic did not know this fact. He's dead, she said to herself.

Then, as the Manager drew the bolt of the side-door, she saw, to her immense relief, Octavius totter out. He was shaking like a leaf, she could see, and the tuft on the end of his bell-pull tail had been scorched off, but he was safe!

By the time the fire engine arrived, the three men had the fire under control, and all that remained was for the firemen to play their hoses on neighbouring buildings to damp them down.

Things could have been much worse.

The rails had burned, the wooden manger too, and Octavius's tack, hung on the smoke-blackened walls, was ruined. But the roof was undamaged, and everything could be put right again.

Only the Manager saw that by a strange chance the flames that had licked at the notice on the open front door had done so selectively. Now it simply read:

"Things could have been much worse," he said to Joe and Jim, when the fire brigade had left.

"We'd have been too late, Boss," the stockman said, "if it hadn't been for Joe's little Tamworth."

"Jim's right," said the pigman. "If she hadn't made all that racket we'd never have noticed in time. Saved the old mule's life, she did."

"And a lot more lives too, I dare say," said the Manager, brushing bits of blackened straw out of his beard. "If that fire had really taken hold, it would have run right down the line of buildings, Dutch barn and all. The Centre would have been pretty well ruined. She's a heroine, that piglet is, and I'll make sure the newspapers hear all about it. Just look at the pair of them now."

The three men looked down the yard, where Octavius, still trembling, was taking a long drink. Then, his thirst quenched, he bent his grey head to his friend, while drips of water fell from his velvety muzzle on to her upturned snout.

"Thank you, my dear little girl," he said simply, and they rubbed noses.

Some weeks passed before Triffic and Octavius could put on their act again. The old mule needed a good rest to recover from the shock, the Manager thought, and anyway the tack had to be replaced, and the sledge, which had also burned.

Meanwhile the loose-box had to be put to rights again and thoroughly cleaned, the walls whitewashed, and the rails and manger replaced.

No one knew for sure what had caused the fire, but there was little doubt in the Manager's mind, and he had a large new notice made and posted by the main gates, which said:

SMOKING IS STRICTLY PROHIBITED ANYWHERE IN THE CENTRE. YOUR CARELESSLY DROPPED CIGARETTE ENDS COULD COST THE LIVES OF THESE ANIMALS. WE WANT OUR RARE BREEDS TO SURVIVE. PLEASE DO NOT SMOKE

Everyone knew, through newspapers and television, of the fire and of the heroic part that the piglet had played (as indeed did all the animals in the Centre, for the pigeons told them), and everyone was waiting eagerly to see the odd couple perform once again. But in the meantime, something else happened.

Triffic went down to the pigsties one morning to say hello to her mother, and was surprised to find the Tamworth's sty besieged by a large crowd.

There was nothing unusual about the sows attracting attention — lots of people came to admire old Molly with her squashed-in face, or the gleaming blackness of Laetitia, or Sarah's saddle, or Glossy's spots, or dark-brown Betty Berkshire with her white forehead and feet and her double chin. But why, this day, was everyone pushing and shoving for a look into one sty only — that of the sandy-red long-snouted Teresa Tamworth?

Triffic stood behind the feet of the jostling crowd, wondering what on earth was happening.

Just then two fantails flew down from the old pepper-pot-shaped dovecot and began to peck around at bits of food that people had dropped.

"What's up?" said Triffic. "Is my Mum all right?"

"She's all right and no mistake," said one of the pigeons.

"Haven't you heard?" said the second pigeon.

"No, what?"

"Happy event," said the first bird.

"Seven happy events," said the other.

"Two boys..."

"...and five girls."

Triffic ran to find Octavius.

"What d'you think!" she squealed excitedly. "I've got two brothers and *five* sisters! Oh Octavius, won't Mum be pleased!"

That evening when all the visitors had gone, Triffic went down to the yard again and stood outside her mother's door.

"Mum!" she called.

"What is it, dear?" said Teresa. "I'm rather busy."

"But Mum, can't I have a look at the new babies?"

"Not just now."

"Later then?"

"We'll see."

"Run along, Triffic, there's a good girl," said Betty Berkshire from next door. "Your mother doesn't want to be bothered."

"Mum doesn't want to be bothered with me any more, Octavius," said Triffic that night.

"It's natural," said Octavius. "All her concern is for her new litter." He gave his feeble bray, half cough, half groan.

"You mustn't be sad about it," he said, "or you will make me feel sad again and that would never do."

"It certainly wouldn't," said Triffic.

She looked at her friend's face, set as usual in an expression of extreme melancholy.

"You *are* happy, Octavius, aren't you?" she said.

"I am, my dear," said the old mule. "So long as I have you."

And he was happier still a couple of days later when they moved back into the renovated loose-box. New tack had been bought, a new sledge constructed, and then, after a period of rehearsals, they were ready for the opening performance, the first since the fire.

The pigman had groomed Triffic with great care, oiling her ginger hair and even cleaning and polishing her trotters.

As for Octavius, the stockman had brushed and curry-combed him till his grey coat shone. His long ears, as usual, would not stand up properly, his upright mane was too short to do much with, and the hair on his tail-tassel had not yet fully grown back, but all the same he looked in fine fettle for such an old fellow. It was hard to remember now that bony despondent-looking wreck upon which Triffic Tamworth had first set eyes.

What a crowd turned up that morning! The great cobbled yard of the Survival Centre was packed with people, clapping and cheering as Triffic and Octavius went through their act.

The Manager stood watching the finale — the driving of Octavius by Triffic, the treacle-smeared reins held in her mouth — and the very latest trick he had taught her — to get off the sledge and then go down on her knees in a last bow to the crowd.

She performed it perfectly, and he stroked his beard and listened to the roars of applause.

Just in front of him a small boy was jumping up and down and shouting with excitement.

"Did you enjoy it?" he said to him.

"Yes!" cried the boy. "It's great! What's his name, mister?"

"Octavius," said the Manager.

"That's a funny name."

"Well, you see, he's the survivor of an eight-mule team."

"No," said the boy. "I don't mean the mule. I mean the pig. What's his name?"

"It isn't a he," said the Manager. "It's a she. And actually, she hasn't got a name."

"She's *triffic*!" said the boy. "That's what she is!"

"O.K." said the Manager. "You said it. She's Triffic."

THE END

Q. How do you get a sick pig to hospital?

A. In a hambulance

Q. And what do you give it for a sore snout?

A. Oinkment

PIGS IN THE DARK

What do you think of the pigs shown here?
Not very good, are they!
Can you draw a pig with your eyes shut?
It's harder than it sounds. Have a go –
and no cheating! (I didn't.)

Dick King-Smith

Giulia

Nick

Piers

Who'd Believe It?

A few years ago three extraordinary pigs caused quite a stir. In fact their snouts were plastered all over local, national and even international newspapers and magazines. Why? Well, they were sheep-pigs!

The three 'little' piggies – one Tamworth hog and two European wild boars – lived at the Gower Farm Museum in South Wales, owned at that time by brothers Clive and Ian Watters. The pigs were free to follow the brothers around the farm as they did their daily chores and the fun began when the pigs started imitating the sheep-dogs and rounding up the sheep. Soon the brothers only needed to call "Piggie! Piggie!" if they needed a helping 'ham'.

Clive and Ian have now sold their farm museum and they keep the two wild boars as pets. But their Tamworth hog has stayed on at the farm museum, and he's still earning his keep, doing what he does best ... rounding up sheep.

Babe, the original Sheep-Pig, says:

Glad I didn't have to give the password in Welsh!

Quiz ?

How much can you remember about the pigs featured in the book? To see how much of a pignoramus you really are here's a quick quiz. The statements are either true or false, so check back in the book to see if what we've said is really just a whopper, a fib, a lie – a porky pie!

1 St Anthony's Pig is the smallest pig in a litter. True or false?

2 The Pig-Faced Lady, exhibited in 1837, was really a hippopotamus dressed in women's clothes. True or false?

3 The recently bred Iron Age pig is a cross between a pure wild boar and a Gloucester Old Spots. True or false?

4 The smallest breed of pig is the Mini Maialino. True or false?

5 The heaviest pig in the world was a Japanese hog called Fatty Fergus. True or false?

6 The piggy bank was first made in the twelfth and thirteenth centuries in China and South-East Asia. True or false?

7 The Tamworth pig is black with floppy ears and a short snout. True or false?

8 The Babirusa is a breed of pig with fourteen tusks. True or false?

9 The country with the largest number of pigs is Luxembourg. True or false?

10 It has been estimated that the worldwide population of pigs is a massive seven hundred and sixty billion. True or false?

How well have you done? Check your answers on page 62

How well have you done? Check your answers on page 62

Doctor, doctor, (or should it be, Vet, Vet), my pig's got no snout

Doctor/Vet How does it smell?

Awful!

If you have any serious enquiries about pigs, then we've listed the addresses of some useful organisations and specialist magazines that might be of interest to you:

British Pig Association
(formerly the National Pig
Breeders' Association)
7 Rickmansworth Road
Watford
Hertfordshire
WD1 7HE

Pig Farming Magazine
Farming Press Ltd
Wharfedale Road
Ipswich
Norfolk
IP1 4LG

Rare Breeds Survival Trust
National Agricultural Centre
Kenilworth
Warwickshire
CV8 2LG

Pig International (UK)
18 Chapel Street
Petersfield
Hampshire
GU32 3DZ

National Pig News
BC Publications
16c Market Place
Diss
Norfolk
IP22 3AB

(There are seventeen Approved Farm Parks for rare breeds in Britain today. Why not contact the RBST and find out where the nearest one is to you – it should be a great day out...)

If you're simply mad about pigs and can't wait to find out more about their record-breaking feats and peculiarities, then we've also listed a couple of the books we consulted, that you might like to read or refer to:

The Guinness Book of Records (updated annually), published by Guinness Publishing Ltd.

Learned Pigs and Fireproof Women, by Ricky Jay, published by Robert Hale Ltd.

QUIZ ANSWERS 1~10

True *(p 23)*
False *(p 29)*
False *(p 51)*
True *(p 10)*
False *(p 10)*
True *(p 42)*
False *(p 26)*
False *(p 45)*
False *(p 37)*
False *(p 37)*

Acknowledgements

I would like to express my gratitude to all those people who have helped to make this book possible, especially: Carlota Robinson of Robinson's Racing Pigs; Charles Baker of Saltford Pottery; David Mercer of Hog Wild!; William L.R. Oliver of the Pigs and Peccaries Specialist Group, IUCN/SSC; Joe Henson of the Cotswold Farm Park and other RBST members; Rob Bartram; David Spector; and Gillian Spector. I would also like to thank the team at Victor Gollancz, including: Chris Kloet, Caroline Bingham, Jane Walsh, Ian Craig, Piers Tilbury and Debra Noakes.
Dick King-Smith

Illustrations:

pp 8, 9, 12-14, 24, 29, 35-37, 46-48, 56-59 © Liz Graham-Yooll; logos on pp 9, 11, 14, 25, 37, 49 © Carlota Robinson; pp 19, 22, 28, 39, 50 © Jan Nesbitt; p 10 © Museum of English Naive Art; pp 11, 60 © Mary Rayner; pp 4-6, 16, 17, 32-34, 49, 54, 55, 59, 62 © Lucy Maddison; p 52 © Alice Englander.

Photographs:

p 5 by kind permission of Penguin Books; p 9 © Lynn M. Stone/Image Bank; p 15 © Åke Lindau/Ardea; p 11 © Carlota Robinson; p 23 © H. Luettike/Zefa; pp 26-27: Gloucester Old Spot, Large Black, Middle White and Berkshire © Marsden & Batley (by arrangement with the British Pig Association); Tamworth Sows © Cotswold Farm Park; Saddleback © John Daniels/Ardea; British Lop © British Lop Society; Oxford Sandy & Black © Oxford Sandy & Black Pig Society; p 31 © Vera Fryer; p 42 © Spink & Son Ltd., London; p 43 © Jim Sparks/Tony Stone Worldwide; pp 44-45: Warthog, Pigmy Pig, Peccary and African Bush Pig © William Oliver; Bearded Pig © Roland Wirth; Giant Forest Hog © Nobuyuki Yamaguchi; Babirusa © Phillip Coffey; all reproduced by courtesy of the IUCN/SSC Pigs and Peccaries Specialist Group; Wild Boar © Stefan Meyers/Ardea; p 51 © Stefan Meyers/Ardea; p 53 © Charles Baker; p 60 © Terry Smith

Dick King-Smith has written a number of other books about pigs. Characters from these books appear on the following pages: *Daggie Dogfoot*, illustrated by Mary Rayner, p 11; *Ace*, illustrated by Liz Graham-Yooll, p 29; *Saddlebottom*, illustrated by Alice Englander, p 52; *The Sheep-Pig*, illustrated by Mary Rayner, p 60.

Other titles by Dick King-Smith include: *Alphabeasts*; *The Fox Busters*; *Harry's Mad*; *The Jenius*; *Magnus Powermouse*; *Martin's Mice*; *The Mouse Butcher*; *Noah's Brother*; *The Queen's Nose*; *The Toby Man*; and *Tumbleweed*.